Spring Harvest
Praise

Copyright and photocopying

Acknowledgements

Scripture quotations taken from the HOLY BIBLE, NEW INTERNATIONAL VERSION.
Copyright © 1973, 1978, 1984 by International Bible Society. Used by permission of Hodder and Stoughton Limited. All rights reserved. "NIV" is a registered trade mark of International Bible Society. UK trademark number 1448790

Music layout, design & type setting by David Ball, davidoxon@aol.com
Cover design by Adept Design
Printed in England by Halcyon

Published by Spring Harvest, 14 Horsted Square, Uckfield, East Sussex, TN22 1QG, UK.
Spring Harvest. A Registered Charity.
Distributed by ICC, Silverdale Road, Eastbourne, East Sussex, BN20 7AB, UK.

Spring Harvest wishes to acknowledge and thank the following people for their help in the compilation and production of this songbook: Andrew Crookall, Trine Crouch, Cheryl Jenkinson, Geraldine Latty, Belinda Patrick, Trish Morgan, John Pantry, David Peacock, Adrian Thompson, and Spring Harvest Head Office staff. Thank you to Marie Birkinshaw, Mark Earey, Andy Flannagan, Nick Harding, Trish Morgan, David Peacock, Richard Stephenson, Steve Thompson, Joy Townhill and Simon Ward for liturgy and worship tips. We are also very grateful to the many worship leaders who have contributed to the song selection process.

ISBN 1 899 78845 X

Contents

Songs are listed in order of first line, not
title. In a few cases, alphabetical ordering
of songs has been changed slightly, in
order to ensure that page turns are not
needed in any two-page songs.

Index

Song titles differing from first lines are in italics

1   Above all powers

Lenny LeBlanc
& Paul Baloche

This song is recorded on the **Spring Harvest 2003 New Songs Album**

2

A love so undeserved
(Amazing)

Matt Redman

Verse

1. A love so un-de-served, a gift that's free, you la-vish on me.
2. For-give-ness runs so deep with-in your heart of lov-ing kind-ness;

A peace I could not earn, and mer-cy for the free-dom of my
and, should a soul for-get, the cross of Christ re-minds us ev-'ry

soul.
day.

Chorus

That's what's so— a-ma-zing a-bout your grace.

That's what's so— a-ma-zing a-bout your grace.

Lord, ev-'ry day you

Suggested guitar groove 'E' (see page 125)
This song is recorded on the Spring Harvest 2003 New Songs Album

pour on me your bles-sings of e-ter-ni-ty. And that's what's so a-ma-

zing a-bout your grace.

Free-ly I've re-ceived, now free-

ly to give.— Free-ly I've re-ceived, now free-ly to give.—

Free-ly I've re-ceived, now free-ly to give,— give my life to you.— (And)

3   # All creation cries to you
(God is great)

Strongly

Marty Sampson

1. All cre-a - tion cries— to you,_____
2. All cre-a - tion gives— you praise,_____
3. All to you,—— O God— we bring._____

wor-ship-ping— in spi-rit and— in truth._____
you a-lone— are tru-ly great,_____
Je-sus teach— us how— to live._____

Glo-ry to—— the Faith-ful One,_____
you a-lone— are God who reigns_____
Let your fi-re burn— in us_____ that

(v.3)

all may hear,— and all— may see.—

Je-sus Christ,— God's Son._____
for e-ter-ni-ty._____

This song is recorded on the Spring Harvest 2002 Live Worship Album & on the double album Celebrating 25 Years of Spring Harvest

(continued over...)

12

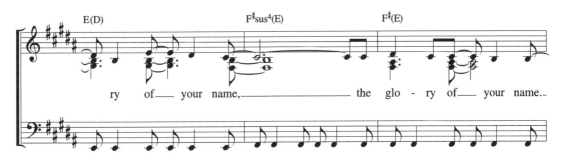

3a   Praise God, all the world

Blessed are you, Lord our God, King of the universe!
To you be glory and praise for ever.

From the rising of the sun to its setting
your name is proclaimed in all the world.
To you be glory and praise for ever.

When the time had fully come
you sent the Sun of Righteousness.
In him the fullness of your glory dwells.
To you be glory and praise for ever.

From New Patterns for Worship (Church House Publishing 2002). Copyright © The Archbishops' Council 2002

4   Alleluia, alleluia, Jesus is the Lord

Moderately

Tony Ryce-Kelly
& Rónán Johnston

Suggested guitar groove 'G' (see page 125)
This song is recorded on the Spring Harvest 2002 New Songs Album, the 2002 Live Worship Album
& on the double album Celebrating 25 Years of Spring Harvest

he's the truth,____ he's the life.____

You're the way,____ you're the truth,____ you're the life.__

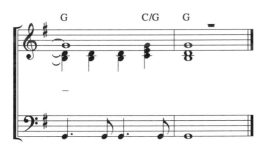

4a   An Easter shout

From John 11: 25

Jesus is the resurrection and the life:
those who believe in him shall never die. Alleluia!

5

All I can bring

John de Jong

Capo 1 (Em)

Moderately

(continued over...)

17

ving you,— my Sa - viour.—— All that I have— is yours,-

— all that I have— is yours.——

2. Teach me your ways—

6

All of you
(Enough)

Chris Tomlin
& Louie Giglio

(continued over...)

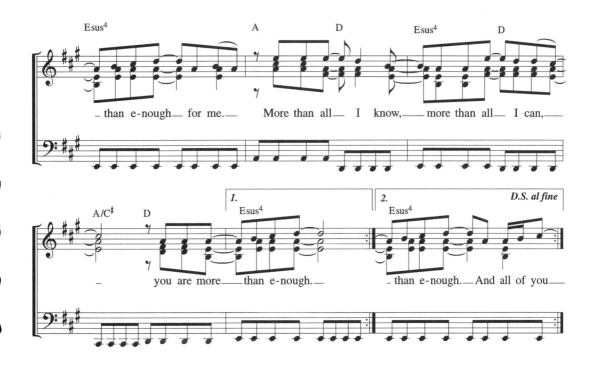

6a Collect for Confession

Almighty God,
who brought into being a new agreement
for the forgiveness of sins
through the perfect sacrifice of your only Son,
forgive the wicked things that we have done and
remember our wrong-doing no more.
Write your teachings on our minds and hearts
and make us your children to be brother and sisters with Jesus Christ,
who lives and reigns with you and
in the unity of the Holy Spirit,
one God now and for ever. Amen.

7

Almighty God

Capo 3(D)

Rhys Scott

Worshipfully

Al - migh - ty—— God, Ho - ly—— One.
—— Lamb, who bore our—— sin.

Who can stand—— be - fore—— you, who can—— come?
Who de - serves—— such mer - cy, gra - cious—— King?

1. *2.* *Chorus*

Per - fect—— I come to your

throne of—— grace, I'm stand - ing— in—— Christ,

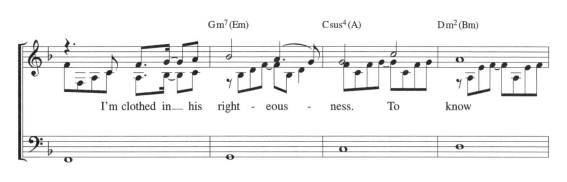

I'm clothed in— his right - eous - ness. To know

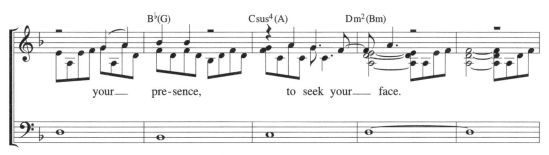

your— pre - sence, to seek your— face.

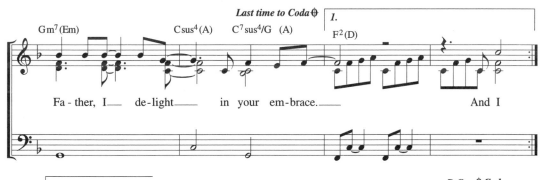

Fa - ther, I— de - light—— in your em - brace.—— And I

— Al - migh - ty— —

8

Amazing grace

AMAZING GRACE

Early American Melody
John Newton (1725-1807)

With feeling

1. A - maz - ing grace! How sweet the sound that saved a
2. 'Twas grace that taught my heart to fear, and grace my
3. Through ma - ny dan - gers, toils and snares I have al -
4. The Lord has pro - mised good to me, his word my
5. Yes, when this heart and flesh shall fail, and mor - tal
6. When we've been there a thou - sand years, bright shin - ing

wretch like me; I once was lost, but now am
fears re - lieved; how pre - cious did that grace ap -
rea - dy come; 'tis grace that brought me safe thus
hope se - cures; he will my shield and por - tion
life shall cease, I shall pos - sess wi - thin the
as the sun, we've no less days to sing God's

found, was blind, but now I see.
pear, the hour I first be - lieved!
far, and grace will lead me home.
be as long as life en - dures.
veil a life of joy and peace.
praise than when we first be - gun.

9

And after all
(Unashamed)

Capo 3(G)

Paul Oakley

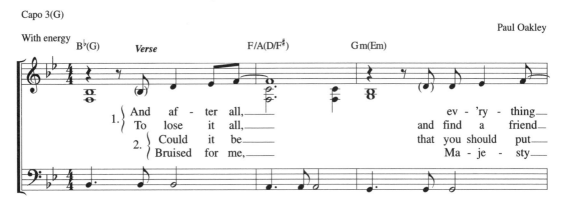

1. And af-ter all,___ ev-'ry-thing___
   To lose it all,___ and find a friend___
2. Could it be___ that you should put___
   Bruised for me,___ Ma-je-sty___

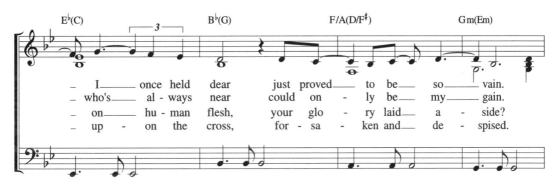

___ I___ once held dear just proved___ to be___ so___ vain.
___ who's___ al-ways near could on-ly be___ my___ gain.
___ on___ hu-man flesh, your glo-ry laid___ a-side?
___ up-on the cross, for-sa-ken and___ de-spised.

(1.) And when I think___ of what___ you've done___ for me,___
(2.) When I think___ of what___ it cost___ for you,___

to bring me to___ the Fa-ther's___ side:

(continued over...)

And can it be

Words: Charles Wesley (1707-88)
Music: Thomas Campbell's Bouquet

Steady 4 ♩ = 86

f

1. And can it be that
2. 'Tis my - stery all! - The Im-
3. He left his Fa - ther's
4. Long my im - pri - soned
5. No con - dem - na - tion

I should gain an in - terest in the Sav - iour's blood?
mor - tal dies, who can ex - plore his strange de - sign?
throne a - bove - so free, so in - fi - nite his grace -
spi - rit lay fast bound in sin and na - ture's night:
now I dread; Je - sus, and all in him, is mine!

Died he for me, who caused his pain; for me, who him to
In vain the first - born se - raph tries to sound the depths of
emp - tied him-self of all but love, and bled for A - dam's
thine eye dif-fused a quick - 'ning ray; I woke the dun - geon
A - live in him, my liv - ing head, and clothed in righ - teous-

11

As angels looked on

James Gregory

1. As an-gels looked on, you humb-led your-self,
2. Your great sa-cri-fice, you gave up your life,

gave up your glo-ri-ous throne. O - be - dient to God,
such was your pas-sion for us. But God raised you up

you came to the earth, full of com-pas-sion for us.
and now hea-ven sings in praise of your glo-ri-ous cross.

What can I do be-fore such love? To your ma - jes-ty I bow.
What can I do be-fore such power? To your ma - je-sty I bow.

12 As we bring our songs of love today
(How long?)

Graham Kendrick

13 Before the throne

Majestically

Music: Vikki Cook
Words: Charitee L Bancroft

1. Be-fore the throne of God a-bove I have a strong, a per-fect plea: a great high priest, whose name is Love, who ev-er lives and pleads for me. My name is writ-ten on his hands, my name is hid-den in his heart; I know that while in heaven he stands no power can force me to de-part;

2. When Sa-tan tempts me to de-spair and tells me of the guilt with-in, up-ward I look, and see him there who made an end of all my sin. Be-cause the sin-less Sa-viour died, my sin-ful soul is count-ed free; for God, the just, is sa-tis-fied to look on him and par-don me.

3. Be-hold him there! The ri-sen Lamb, my per-fect, sin-less right-eous-ness, the great un-change-a-ble 'I Am', the King of glo-ry and of grace! One with my Lord I can-not die: my soul is pur-chased by his blood, my life is safe with Christ on high, with Christ, my Sa-viour and my

Suggested guitar groove 'H' (see page 125)

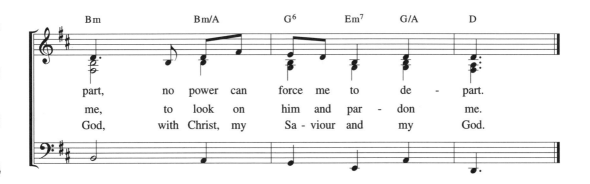

	Bm	Bm/A	G⁶	Em⁷	G/A	D

part,   no   power   can   force   me   to   de -   part.

me,   to   look   on   him   and   par - don   me.

God,   with Christ, my   Sa - viour and   my   God.

13a Gloria in Excelsis

Glory to God in the highest,
and peace to his people on earth.
Lord God, heavenly King,
almighty God and Father,
we worship you, we give you thanks,
we praise you for your glory.

Lord Jesus Christ, only Son of the Father,
Lord God, Lamb of God,
you take away the sin of the world:
have mercy on us;
you are seated at the right hand of the Father:
receive our prayer.

For you alone are the Holy One,
you alone are the Lord,
you alone are the Most High, Jesus Christ,
with the Holy Spirit,
in the glory of God the Father.
Amen.

14   Befriended

Matt Redman

1. Be - friend - ed, be - friend - ed by the King a - bove all kings.
   - - vi - ted, in - vi - ted deep in - to this my - ste - ry.
   - - stoun - ded, a - stoun - ded that your go - spel beck - oned me.

Sur - ren - dered, sur - ren - dered to the friend a - bove all friends.
De - ligh - ted, de - ligh - ted by the won - ders I have seen.
Sur - roun - ded, sur - roun - ded, but I've ne - ver been so free.

2. In -

This will be my sto - ry, this will be my

15 Be lifted up
(Let the heavens rejoice)

Paul Oakley

Slow 4

Be lif - ted___ up, be lif - ted___ up. As we bow___ down, be lif - ted___ up. Be lif - ted___ be lif - ted___ up. *(Fine)* Let the hea - vens re - joice,___ let the na - tions be glad.___ Let the whole earth trem - ble, for you are God.___ Come and wor - ship the Lord___ in the beau - ty of ho - li - ness.___

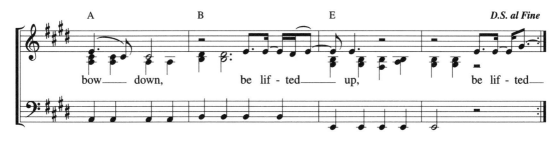

15a Call to worship

Psalm 95: 6 & 7a

Come, let us bow down in worship,
    let us kneel before the Lord our Maker;
for he is our God
    and we are the people of his pasture,
    the flock under his care.

16   Be thou my vision

Words: Tr. Mary Elizabeth Byrne (1880-1931)
& Eleanor Henrietta Hull (1860-1935)
Music: Ancient Irish melody

Quietly, building with strength

1. Be thou my vi - sion, O Lord of my heart.
2. Be thou my wis - dom, be thou my true word,
3. Be thou my breast-plate, my sword for the fight,
4. Rich - es I heed not, nor man's emp - ty praise,
5. O high King of hea - ven, when bat - tle is done

Nought be all else to me, save that thou art.
I e - ver with thee, and thou with me, Lord.
be thou my ar - mour and be thou my might.
thou my in - he - ri - tance now and al - ways.
grant hea - ven's joy to me, bright hea - ven's sun.

Thou my best thought in the day and the night,
Thou my great Fa - ther and I thy true son,
Be my soul's shel - ter, and thou my high tower,
Thou and thou on - ly, the first in my heart,
Christ of my own heart, what - e - ver be - fall,

Suggested guitar groove 'C' (see page 125)
This song is recorded on the double album Celebrating 25 Years of Spring Harvest

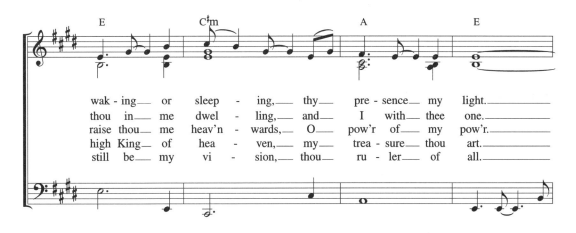

wak - ing___ or sleep - ing,___ thy___ pre - sence___ my light.___
thou in___ me dwel - ling,___ and___ I with___ thee one.___
raise thou___ me heav'n - wards,___ O___ pow'r of___ my pow'r.___
high King___ of hea - ven,___ my___ trea - sure thou art.___
still be___ my vi - sion, thou___ ru - ler___ of all.___

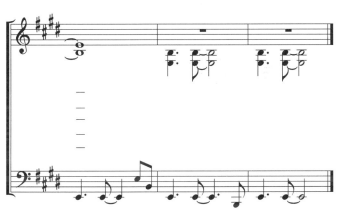

16a Prayer for the Unity of the Church (1)

Heavenly Father,
you have called us in the Body of your Son Jesus Christ
to continue his work of reconciliation
and reveal you to the world:
forgive us the sins which tear us apart;
give us the courage to overcome our fears
and to seek that unity which is your gift and your will;
through Jesus Christ your Son our Lord. **Amen.**

From Common Worship: Services and Prayers for the Church of England. Copyright © The Archbishops' Council 2000

17 Blessed be your name

Beth & Matt Redman

Suggested guitar groove 'F' (see page 125)

way.   My heart will choose to say,   'Lord,

bles-sed be   your   name,—   you   name.'—   Bles-sed be the

17a Be joyful in suffering
Habakkuk 3: 17 & 18

Though the fig-tree does not bud
        and there are no grapes on the vines,
though the olive crop fails
        and the fields produce no food,
though there are no sheep in the pen
        and no cattle in the stalls,
yet I will rejoice in the Lord,
        I will be joyful in God my Saviour.

18 Christ be before me

Phil Hart

Simply

Christ be be-fore — me, Christ be be-side — me, Christ — be all — a - round.

Instrumental

19 Christ the eternal Lord

With strength ♩ = 120

Words: Timothy Dudley-Smith
Music: George Elvey

1. Christ the e-ter-nal Lord whose pro-mise here we claim, whose gifts of grace are free-ly— poured on all who name your name; with thank-ful-ness and praise we stand be-fore your throne, in-
2. Christ the un-chang-ing word to ev-ery pass-ing age, whose time-less teach-ings still are— heard set forth on scrip-ture's page; trans-form our thought and mind, en-ligh-ten all who read, with-
3. Christ the re-deem-ing Son who shares our hu-man birth, and by his death sal-va-tion— won for e-very child of earth; in-spire our hearts, we pray, to tell your love a-broad, that
4. Christ the un-fad-ing light of e-ver-last-ing day, our morn-ing star in splen-dour— bright, the life, the truth, the way; that light of truth you give to ser-vants as to friends, your
5. Christ the a-scen-ded King ex-al-ted high a-bove, whose praise un-end-ing a-ges— sing, whom yet un-seen we love; when mor-tal life is past your voice from hea-ven's throne shall

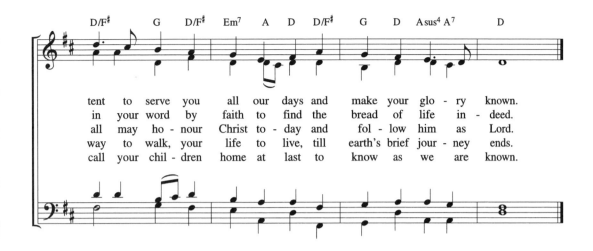

tent	to	serve	you	all	our	days	and	make	your	glo -	ry	known.
in	your	word	by	faith	to	find	the	bread	of	life	in -	deed.
all	may	ho - nour	Christ	to -	day	and	fol -	low	him	as	Lord.
way	to	walk,	your	life	to	live,	till	earth's	brief	jour - ney	ends.
call	your	chil - dren	home	at	last	to	know	as	we	are	known.

19a Confesson from Evening Prayer

Most merciful God,
Father of our Lord Jesus Christ,
we confess that we have sinned
in thought, word and deed.
We have not loved you with our whole heart.
We have not loved our neighbours as ourselves.
In your mercy
forgive what we have been,
help us to amend what we are,
and direct what we shall be;
that we may do justly,
love mercy,
and walk humbly with you, our God.
Amen.

From Common Worship: Services and Prayers for the Church of England. Copyright © The Archbishops' Council 2000

20 Christ the Lord is risen today

Words: Charles Wesley (1707-88)
Music: *Lyra Davidica*, 1708
Arr. W A Monk (1823-89)

1. Christ the Lord is ris'n to-day;— al - le - lu - jah!
2. Love's re - deem - ing work is done,—
3. Lives a - gain our glo - rious King;—
4. Soar we now where Christ hath led,—
5. King of glo - ry! Soul of bliss!—

Sons of men and an - gels say:— al - le - lu - jah!
Fought the fight, the bat - tle won;—
Where, O death, is now thy sting?—
Fol - lowing our ex - al - ted Head;—
E - ver - last - ing life is this,—

Raise your joys and tri - umphs high;— al - le - lu - jah!
Vain the stone, the watch, the seal;—
Once he died our souls to save;—
Made like him, like him we rise;—
Thee to know, thy pow'r to prove,—

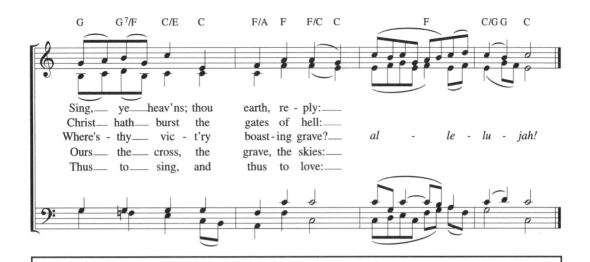

| G | G⁷/F | C/E | C | | F/A | F | F/C | C | | F | | C/G G | C |

Sing,— ye—heav'ns; thou earth, re-ply:—
Christ— hath— burst the gates of hell:—
Where's-thy— vic-t'ry boast-ing grave?— al - le - lu - jah!
Ours— the— cross, the grave, the skies:—
Thus— to— sing, and thus to love:—

20a The Great 'I Am'

From Exodus 3, John 1 and Ephesians 1 & 3

Hear, God's people,
the Lord our God, the Lord is one.

**He is the God of Abraham and Sarah,
the God of Isaac, the God of Jacob.**

He is the God who says, 'I am who I am,'
his name for ever and his title for all generations.

**He is the God and Father of our Lord Jesus Christ,
the one from whom every family on earth is named.**

He is the eternal Word,
through whom all things were made.

**He lived among us, full of grace and truth,
bringing life and light to all creation.**

He is the Spirit who strengthens us in our inner being:
he reveals the love of Christ and fills us with the fullness of God.

Hear God's people, the Lord our God is three in one.
We believe in one God, Father, Son and Holy Spirit. Amen.

21 Clothed with splendour
(Awesome God)

Andy Bromley

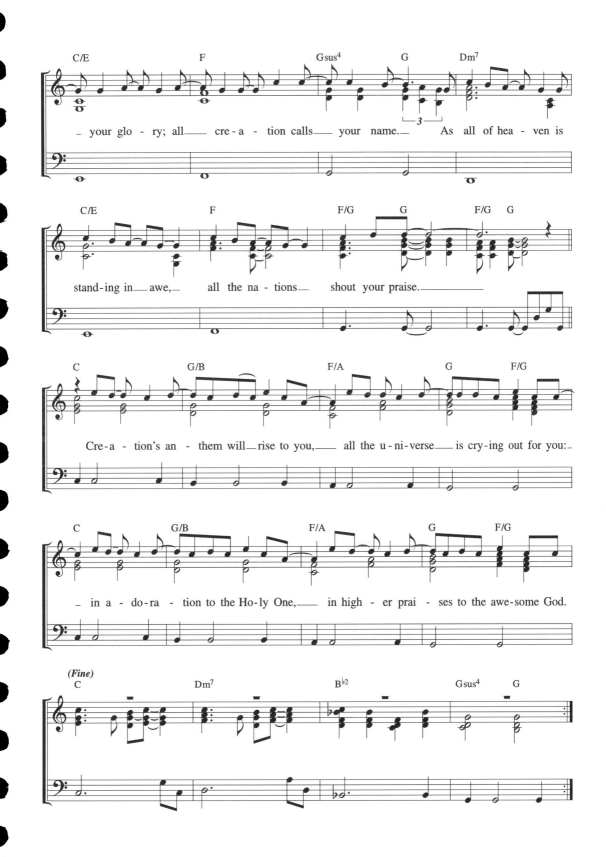

22   Come, now is the time to worship

Steadily

Brian Doerksen

Suggested guitar groove 'A' or 'D' (see page 125)

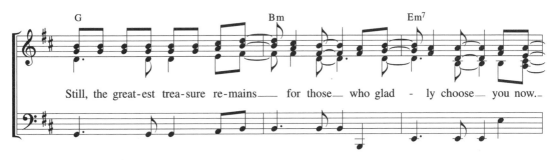

Still, the great-est trea-sure re-mains___ for those___ who glad - ly choose___ you now.___

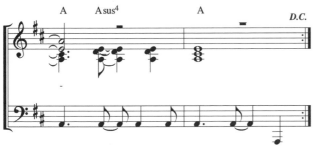

22a Worthy of worship

Psalm 86: 8–10

Among the gods there is none like you, O Lord;
    no deeds can compare with yours.
All the nations you have made
    will come and worship before you, O Lord;
    they will bring glory to your name.
For you are great and do marvellous deeds;
    you alone are God.

23 Come, praise the Lord
(Every breath)

Kristyn Lennox
& Keith Getty

1. Come, praise the Lord,— he is life— in all its full - ness;—
2. Come, praise the Lord,— he is love— that wel-comes sin - ners;—

will you lift your— voice?———— Come, praise the Lord,— he is light—
will you give your— life?———— Come, praise the Lord,— he is great—

— that shat-ters dark - ness;———— we have come to— re-joice.—
— a - bove all o - thers;———— all his ways are— right.—

All a-round the world he is call - ing—— peo-ple who would take up his call

24 Crown him with many crowns

With strength ♩ = 120

Words: Matthew Bridges (1800-94)
& Godfrey Thring (1823-1903)
Music: George Elvey

1. Crown him with ma — ny crowns, the Lamb up — on his throne; hark, how the heaven — ly an — them_drowns all mu — sic but its own! A — wake, my soul, and sing of
2. Crown him the Lord of life, who tri — umphed o'er the grave and rose vic — to — rious in the_strife for those he came to save: his glo — ries now we sing, who
3. Crown him the Lord of love; be — hold his hands and side, those wounds yet vi — si — ble a — bove in beau — ty glo — ri — fied: no an — gel in the sky can
4. Crown him the Lord of peace, whose power a scep — tre sways from pole to pole, that wars may_cease, and all be prayer and praise: his reign shall know no end, and
5. Crown him the Lord of years, the po — ten — tate of time, cre — a — tor of the rol — ling_spheres, in — ef — fa — bly sub — lime! All hail, Re — dee — mer, hail! For

him who died for thee, and hail him as thy
died and rose on high, who died e - ter - nal
ful - ly bear that sight, but down - ward bends his
round his pier - cèd feet fair flowers of pa - ra -
thou hast died for me; thy praise shall ne - ver,

match - less King through all e - ter - ni - ty.
life to bring and lives that death may die.
burn - ing eye at my - ste - ries so bright.
dise ex - tend their fra - grance e - ver sweet.
ne - ver fail through - out e - ter - ni - ty.

24a Christ is Risen

Alleluia! Christ in risen:
he is risen indeed. Alleluia!

Praise the God and Father of our Lord Jesus Christ:
**he has given us new life and hope
by raising Jesus from the dead!**

Alleluia! Christ is risen:
he is risen indeed. Alleluia!

Deep in my heart

Silke Dürrkopf

1. Deep in my heart burns a de - sire,— oh—Lord,——— and I
2. On - ly in you is there a peace— that—lasts,——— Fa - ther,

run——— to you,—— in - to——— your arms.——
in——— your arms,—— there I——— find rest.——

No - thing holds, holds— me back,—— no - thing holds, holds— me— back,—
Your love— it heals,—— your love— it— heals,—

– I come— to you.
– it heals— my heart. Oh

This song was one of many written by foreign aid workers who were arrested by the Taliban and endured 4 months of imprisonment in various jails throughout the autumn of 2001. They were facing uncertainty regarding the safety of their lives but were miraculously rescued in November 2001 by allied foreces in Afghanistan.

Je-sus, Je-sus, Je-sus you are won-der-ful,_____ and a-gain I lay my life in-to your_____

_ hands._____ I bow my knees in awe of your ma-je-sty;_____

deep from_ my____ heart____ you make_ me____ sing.____

25a Trust in the Lord

Psalm 62: 5–8

Find rest, O my soul, in God alone;
    my hope comes from him.
He alone is my rock and my salvation;
    he is my fortress, I shall not be shaken.
My salvation and my honour depend on God;
    he is my mighty rock, my refuge.
Trust in him at all times, O people;
    pour out your hearts to him,
        for God is our refuge.

26 Father into your courts
(All the earth)

Andrew Ulugia
& Wayne Huirua

This song is recorded on the **Spring Harvest 2003 New Songs Album**

fields will ex-alt, seas re-sound. Hear the trees' joy-ful cry, prais-ing you and so will I. A new song I'll sing, Lord, I will glo-ri-fy and bless your ho-ly name. glo-ri-fy and bless your name, glo-ri-fy and bless your name.

27 From every corner of the earth
(Calling all nations)

Slightly driving

Mark Tedder

From ev-'ry cor - ner— of— the— earth— we
will de-clare— your— worth,— your splen-dour— is— re-nowned—
— through all you've— done.— From
sea to shin-ing sea— your glo-ry will— be seen,— through

those that you have called to bear your word.

Esus⁴ *Chorus*

We're call-ing all na - tions to your side, ev-'ry peo-

ple, tongue and tribe, this ge-ne-ra - tion shall de-clare

that you are God. All of the na-

tions will re - joice and we will be your voice

(continued over...)

as we spread___ the awe - some news___ that you're a -

live!

From ev - 'ry cor -

27a Jesus Christ is Lord

Philippians 2: 9–11

Therefore God exalted him to the highest place
    and gave him the name that is above every name,
that at the name of Jesus every knee should bow,
    in heaven and on earth and under the earth,
and every tongue confess that Jesus Christ is Lord,
    to the glory of God the Father.

Bridges to C

28

From heaven you came
(*Servant King*)

Capo 3(C)

Graham Kendrick

Worshipfully

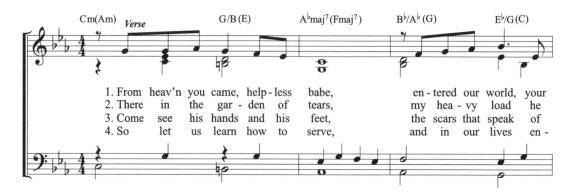

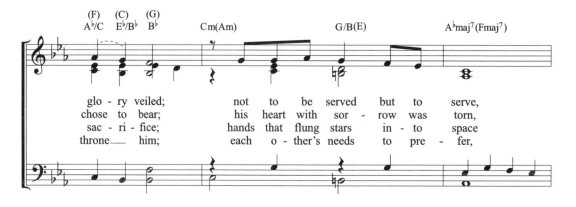

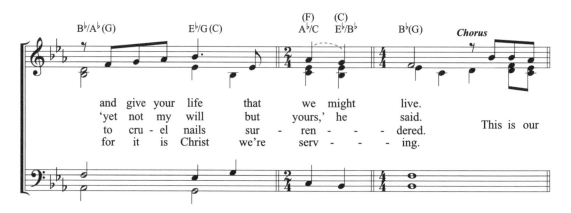

Suggested guitar groove 'C' (see page 125)
This song is recorded on the Spring Harvest 20 Years Double Album

God,— the ser-vant King,— he calls us now to fol-low him,— to bring our
lives as a dai-ly of-fer-ing of wor-ship to— the ser-vant King.

King.

28a We have a great High Priest

From Hebrews 4: 16

Let us hold firmly to the faith we profess:

**We have a great High Priest
who has gone into the very presence of God;
one who can feel sympathy for our weakness,
who was tempted in every way that we are
but did not sin –
Jesus, the Son of God.**

**Let us have confidence and approach God's throne,
where we will receive mercy and grace to help us when we need it.
Amen.**

Bible Praying by Michael Perry (Harper Collins, 1992). Copyright© 1992 Michael Perry

29

Give thanks to the Lord
(Forever)

Chris Tomlin

Moderato

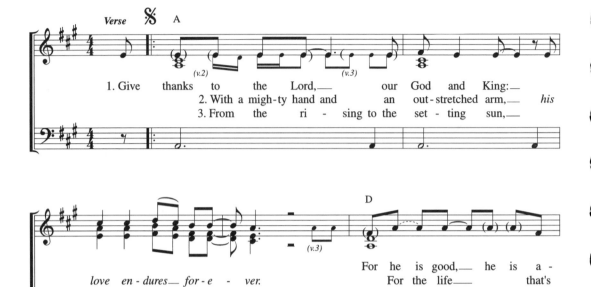

1. Give thanks to the Lord,— our God and King:—
2. With a migh-ty hand and an out-stretched arm,— *his*
3. From the ri - sing to the set - ting sun,—

love en - dures— for - e - ver. For he is good, he is a -
For the life— that's
By the grace of— God,— we will

bove all things.— Sing praise,—
been re - born.— *His love en - dures— for - e - ver.* Sing praise,—
car - ry on.—

sing praise.—
praise,— sing

Suggested guitar groove 'F' (see page 125)
This song is recorded on the Spring Harvest 2002 New Songs Album

30 God Almighty, we look to thee
(Call for mercy)

Judy Bailey

Thoughtfully

1. God Al-migh - ty, we look to thee,— our hearts are hea-
(2.) mis-sing, for those who wait,— for an-ger that

- vy so yours must— bleed. We pray for the
threa - tens to turn in - to hate. We pray for your

vic - tims of tra-ge-dy,— that by your grace, O Lord, some-
pre - sence in their— pain, and ask that you re-veal your-

how they'll find re - lief. For all who suf-fer we are call-ing on you, Lord. O—
self in Je - sus' name.

(continued over...)

Additional verse:
For nations evading the reality still,
for those steeped in denial,
for the silence that kills;
we pray for the governments that are overwhelmed,
secure their people's future,
shine your light on them.

31

God gave us his Son
(I am not ashamed)

Capo 3(D)

Steadily

Kate & Miles Simmonds

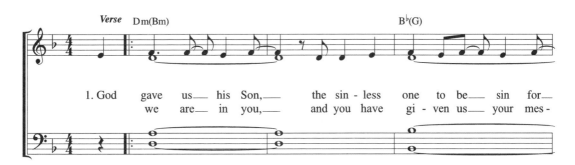

1. God gave us his Son, the sin-less one to be sin for
we are in you, and you have gi-ven us your mes-

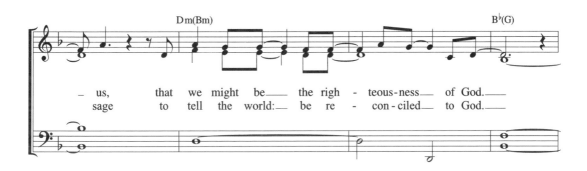

_ us, that we might be the righ - teous-ness of God.
sage to tell the world: be re - con-ciled to God.

Your king - dom has come, we're be-ing changed in-to your like-
Your fa - vour is here in this day of sal - va - tion.

ness; chil - dren of light, it's our time to a - rise.
Now is the time, let your glo - ry a - rise!

(continued over...)

32

God is good

Russ Hughes

33 Great is thy faithfulness

Words: Thomas O Chisolm
Music: William M Runyan

1. Great is thy faith-ful-ness, O God my Fa-ther, there is no
2. Sum-mer and win-ter, and spring-time and har-vest, sun, moon and
3. Par-don for sin and a peace that en-du-reth, thine own dear

sha-dow of turn-ing with thee; thou chang-est not, thy com-
stars in their cour-ses a-bove, join with all na-ture in
pre-sence to cheer and to guide; strength for to-day and bright

pas-sions, they fail not; as thou hast been thou for e-ver wilt be.
ma-ni-fold wit-ness to thy great faith-ful-ness, mer-cy and love.
hope for to-mor-row, bles-sings all mine, with ten thou-sand be-side!

Chorus

Great is thy faith-ful-ness! Great is thy faith-ful-ness! Morn-ing by

morn-ing new mer-cies I see; all I have need-ed thy hand has pro -

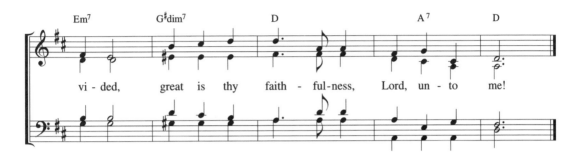

vi-ded, great is thy faith - ful-ness, Lord, un - to me!

33a The Lord's Prayer

Our Father in heaven,
hallowed be your name,
your kingdom come,
your will be done,
on earth as in heaven.
Give us today our daily bread.
Forgive us our sins
as we forgive those who sin against us.
Lead us not into temptation
but deliver us from evil.
For the kingdom, the power,
and the glory are yours
now and for ever.
Amen.

34 Great is your faithfulness
(Unchanging)

35   Greater grace

Chris Bowater

1. Great-er grace, deep-er mer-cy,— wid-er love, high-er ways. Per-fect peace, com-plete for-give-ness,— it's all found— in you, it's all found— in you. 2. More than you.

hope, full as-sur-rance,— joy that more than sa-tis-fies. Com-fort, strength, pow'r and heal-ing,—

It's all found— in you, Je-sus,— it's all found— in

37   Guide me O thou great Jehovah

CWM RHONDDA

Music: John Hughes (1873-1932)
Words: William Williams (1717-91)
Tr. Peter Williams (1727-96)

1. Guide me, O thou great Je-ho-vah, pil-grim through this bar-ren land; I am weak, but thou art might-y, hold me with thy power-ful hand: bread of hea-ven, bread of hea-ven, feed me now and e-ver more, feed me now and e-ver more. (e-ver more)

2. O-pen thou the cry-stal foun-tain whence the heal-ing stream doth flow; let the fie-ry, clou-dy pil-lar lead me all my jour-ney through: strong de-li-v'rer, strong de-li-v'rer, be thou still my strength and shield, be thou still my strength and shield. (strength and shield)

3. When I tread the verge of Jor-dan bid my an-xious fears sub-side; death of death, and hell's de-struc-tion, land me safe on Ca-naan's side: songs of prai-ses, songs of prai-ses, I will e-ver give to thee, I will e-ver give to thee. (give to thee)

38 Have mercy on me

Graham Kendrick

♩ = 110

Have mer-cy on me, O God, (have mer-cy on me, O God,) and hear
my prayer. Have mer-cy on me, O God, (have
mer-cy on me, O God,) and hear my prayer.—

39 Hear my prayer, O Lord

Psalm 61

Debbie Owens

Steadily

40   He is the Lord
(Show your power)

Strong and rhythmic

Kevin Prosch

Suggested guitar groove 'A' (see page 125)
This song is recorded on the Spring Harvest Ultimate Praise Mix Album

41 Here I stand
(To you)

Darlene Zschech

Steadily

Verse

Here I stand,⸺⸺⸺ for - e - ver in⸺ your migh -
⸺⸺⸺ sur - ren - dered whol - ly to⸺

- ty hand,⸺ liv - ing with⸺ your pro - mise⸺
⸺ you,⸺ you set me in⸺ your fam - i - ly,

writ - ten on⸺ my heart.⸺ I am yours⸺
call - ing me⸺ your own.⸺

Now⸺ I,⸺ I be - long⸺ to you,⸺ all I need,⸺
⸺ I⸺ will lift⸺ my hands⸺ to the King,

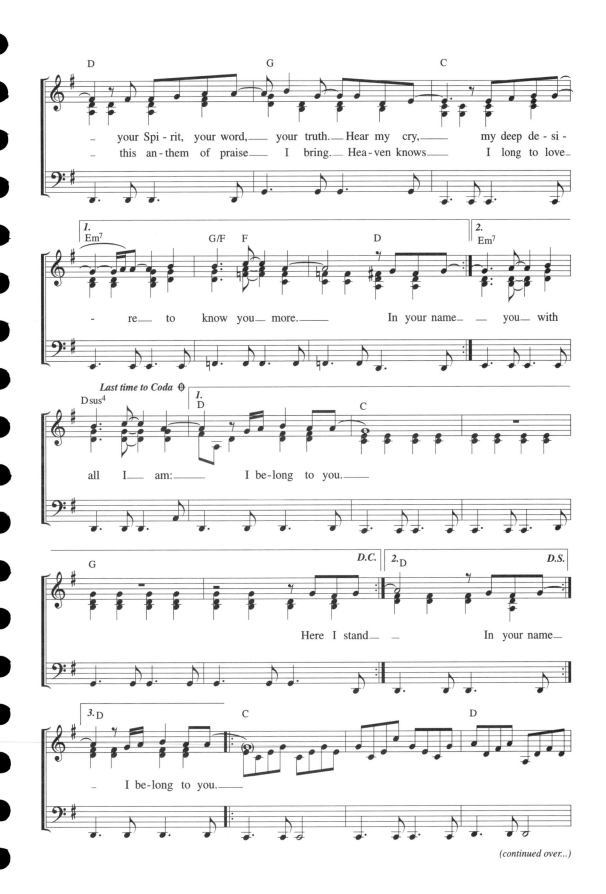

(continued over...)

42

Here is love

DIM OND JESU

Words: William Rees
Music: Robert Lowry (1826-99)

Capo 1(G)

1. Here is love vast as the o-cean,— lov-ing kind-ness as the
2. On the mount of cru-ci-fi-xion— foun-tains o-pened deep and

flood, when the Prince of life, our ran-som— shed for us his pre-cious
wide; through the flood-gates of God's mer-cy— flowed a vast and gra-cious

blood. Who his love will not re-mem-ber?— Who can cease to sing his
tide. Grace and love, like migh-ty ri-vers,— poured in-ces-sant from a-

praise?— He can ne-ver be for-got-ten— through-out heaven's e-ter-nal days.
bove, and hea-ven's peace and per-fect jus-tice— kissed a guil-ty world in love.

Suggested guitar groove 'H' (see page 125)

43

Hold my hand
(Son of God)

Lincoln Brewster
& Marty Sampson

(continued over...)

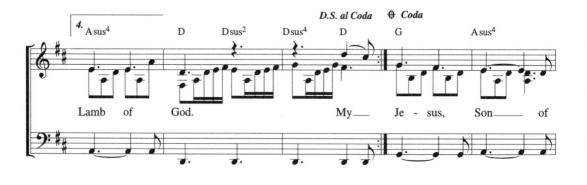

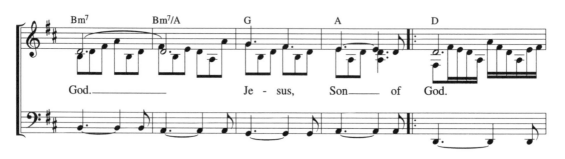

43a Jesus – the light of the world

John 8: 12

When Jesus spoke again to the people, he said, 'I am the light of the world. Whoever follows me will never walk in darkness, but will have the light of life.'

44 Holy, holy God Almighty

Brenton Brown

With drive ♩ = 100

Ho-ly, ho-ly__ God Al-migh-ty,__ who was and is to come.__
God of glo-ry,__ you're so wor-thy,__

all the saints__ bow__ down.__ all the saints bow__

down.__ Ho-ly is__ your name__ in all__ the earth.__

Right-eous are__ your ways,__ so mer-ci-ful.__

E-v'ry-thing__you've done__ is just__ and true.__ Ho-ly, ho-

(continued over...)

This song is recorded on the Spring Harvest 2003 New Songs Album

Coda

down.

God of glo - ry,—— you're so wor - thy,——

1.2.3.

all the saints bow—— down.——

4.

—— down.——

44a The Apostles' Creed

We believe in God, the Father almighty,
creator of heaven and earth.

We believe in Jesus Christ, his only Son, our Lord,
who was conceived by the Holy Spirit,
born of the Virgin Mary,
suffered under Pontius Pilate,
was crucified, died, and was buried;
he descended to the dead.
On the third day he rose again;
he ascended into heaven,
he is seated at the right hand of the Father,
and he will come to judge the living and the dead.

We believe in the Holy Spirit,
the holy catholic Church,
the communion of saints,
the forgiveness of sins,
the resurrection of the body,
and the life everlasting.
Amen.

From Common Worship: Services and Prayers for the Church of England. Copyright © The Archbishops' Council 2000

45 Holy, holy, holy, Lord God Almighty

NICEA
Capo 2(C)

Music: John Bacchus Dykes (1823-76)
Words: Reginald Heber (1783-1826)

With strength

1. Ho-ly, ho-ly, ho - ly, Lord___ God Al - migh - ty! Ear - ly in the morn - ing our song shall rise to thee: ho-ly, ho-ly, ho - ly, mer - ci - ful and migh - ty, God in three per - sons, bles-sèd Tri - ni - ty!

2. Ho-ly, ho-ly, ho - ly! all the saints a - dore thee, cast - ing down their gol - den crowns a - round the glas - sy sea; che - ru-bim and se - ra-phim fal - ling down be - fore thee, who was and is and e - ver more shall be.

3. Ho-ly, ho-ly, ho - ly! though the dark-ness hide thee, though the eye of sin - ful man thy glo - ry may not see; on - ly thou art ho - ly, there is none be - side thee, per - fect in power, in love and pu - ri - ty.

4. Ho-ly, ho-ly, ho - ly, Lord___ God Al - migh - ty! All thy works shall praise thy name in earth, and sky, and sea; ho-ly, ho-ly, ho - ly, mer - ci - ful and migh - ty, God in three per - sons, bles-sèd Tri - ni - ty!

46 Holy Spirit, how I love you

Peter Brooks, Stuart Townend
& Kate Simmonds

Slowly, with feeling

Ho - ly Spi - rit, how I love— you; Ho - ly Spi - rit, flood my soul.—

Ho - ly Spi - rit, take me o - ver; Ho - ly Spi - rit, lead me on. You're the

strength that helps me in my weak - ness, you're the friend who comes to walk be -

side; you're the peace that pas - ses un - der - stand - ing, as you reign in my life.

47 How could I but love you?

Tommy Walker

48 I behold your power and glory
(Irresistible)

Moderately

Darlene Zschech

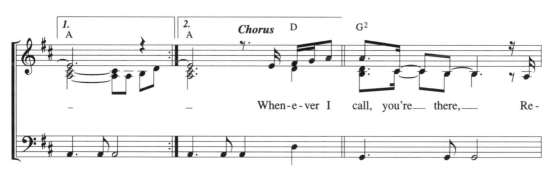

Verse:
I be-hold your pow'r and glo-ry, bring an off-'ring, come be-fore you; wor-ship you, Lord, in the beau-ty of your ho-li-ness.

Chorus:
When-e-ver I call, you're there, Re-deem-er and friend, che-rished be-yond all words, this

49 I belong to you

Trish Morgan

Steady 4

I be-long to you, kee-per of my ways. I be-long to you, plan-ner of my days, through this walk of life, to my fi - nal breath, oh I, oh I, I be-long to you. You reign for-e - ver, high-ly ex-al - ted, hea-ven is hear-ing e-

ter - nal love songs. Praise to our Ma - ker, our God and Sa - viour, cre -

a - tion a - waits___ the com - ing King.

49a Be with us

Be with us, Father of all,
be with us.

Live in us, Son of life,
live in us.

Move in us, Spirit of heaven,
move in us. Amen.

Copyright © Nick Harding

50 If it wasn't for your mercy
(Where angels fear to tread)

Deut 4: 24, 31; Ps 130: 3-4; Heb 12:29

Capo 2(D)

Matt Redman
& Tom Lane

1. If it wasn't for your mer - cy, if it wasn't for your love,
(2.) wasn't for your clean - sing, if it wasn't for your blood,

if it wasn't for your kind - ness, how could I stand?____
if it wasn't for your good - ness, how could I stand?____

2. If it And yet I find my-self a-gain____ where e-ven
(And I)

an - gels fear____ to tread; where I would ne - ver dare____ to come,____

but for the clean - sing of____ your blood.____ 3. With

111

51 I have heard so many songs
(The Father's song)

Capo 1(D)
Gently

Matt Redman

I have heard so ma-ny songs, lis-tened to a
The Fa-ther's song, the Fa-ther's love, you sung it o-ver

thou-sand tongues, but there is one___ that sounds a-bove them all.___
me and for e-ter-ni-ty___ it's

writ-ten on my___ heart.___

Chorus

Hea-ven's per-fect me-lo-dy,___ the cre-a-tor's___

_ sym-pho-ny,___ you are___ sing-ing___ o-ver me___

This song is recorded on the Spring Harvest 2001 New Songs Album

(continued over...)

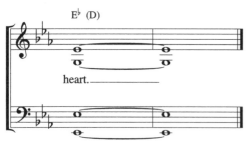

51a The Father's song

Zephaniah 3: 17

The Lord your God is with you,
    he is mighty to save.
He will take great delight in you,
    he will quiet you with his love,
        he will rejoice over you with singing.

Guitar Grooves 1

Introduction

As modern worship songs begin to spring more and more from the band context, there is an increasing need for rhythmic instruction that cannot be communicated by the classic keyboard arrangement alone.

These pages are here to help guitarists get the most out of this book. Left to ourselves we often lapse into our default strumming patterns. With the dual challenges of leading small group worship and playing with a band it is essential to have solid rhythmic foundations that will enable us as guitarists to play both confidently and in a way that enables a band to groove.

Rhythm is the job of the strumming hand (RH), and before focusing on the fretting hand (LH) in the chord charts, we will look at how to build an effortless RH style that can be applied to any of the songs in this book. The main feature of good RH technique is keeping a constant 'down, up' motion no matter what rhythm is being played.

Practice step	Eighth note groove	Sixteenth note groove
1. Move your RH in a constant down (⊓) and up (V) motion, strumming an open E chord. Tap a foot with every downstroke to give you a 1/8th note groove or every other downstroke for a 1/16th note groove		
2. Get hold of a metronome. Set it to 65 bpm and tap your foot on each click (beat). Start strumming either an 1/8th or a 1/16th note groove as in the first step	Your foot should coincide with the click and your RH goes 'down, up' in the space of each beat	Your foot should coincide with the click and your RH goes 'down, up, down, up' in the space of each beat
3. Stop playing. With the metronome still going and your foot tapping with each click, count aloud according to diagrams opposite '+' means say 'and' 'e' means say 'ee' 'a' means say 'a' (as in apple)	1 + 2 + 3 + 4 + The numbers should coincide with the click and the '+'s should all occur in between clicks	1 e + a 2 e + a 3 e + a 4 e + a The numbers should all still coincide with the click
4. Repeat step 3 but this time after a while, start strumming. Keep counting out loud and keep that foot tapping!	1 + 2 + 3 + 4 +	1 e + a 2 e + a 3 e + a 4 e + a
5. This step introduces RH rests. A good guitarist can use a rest (r) as a percussive effect. Hit all the strings at once with your RH palm. Try the following rhythms	1 + 2 + 3 + 4 +	1 e + a 2 e + a 3 e + a 4 e + a
6. Try the following rhythms noting that sometimes a box is left blank. In these cases, keep the RH 'down, up' pattern going but miss the strings! Keep counting and tapping	1 + 2 + 3 + 4 +	1 e + a 2 e + a 3 e + a 4 e + a

Richard Stephenson & Andy Flannagan

Please turn to pg 125 for the strumming patterns for songs in this book.

52

I'm making melody
in my heart to you

Matt Redman

name? How can souls not sing your

praise? Je - sus, you've put

mu - sic in my soul.

last time D.S. *To end*

rit last time.......

53 Image of invisible God

Steadily, with majesty

Stuart Townend
& J.K. Jamieson

1. I - mage of in - vi - si - ble God,
2. Ho - ly One whom an - gels at - tend,
3. There - fore I will not be a - fraid,

cre - a - tor and su - stai - ner of all;
righ - teous King who calls me his friend;
though moun - tains fall and ri - vers may rage;

the King who came to ran - som my soul,
the Prince who of - fers peace with - out end,
I'm safe with - in the ci - ty you've made,

thank you for your per - fect love.
thank you for your per - fect love.
thank you for your per - fect love.

1st time D.C.

Chorus

And it's

you, O Lord,— you're all that I— could ask— for, and in
you, O Lord,— who gives me strength— to fol - low, and in

you, O Lord,— I find the deep - est joy:—
you, O Lord,— is grace for e - v'ry day:—

foun - tain of life,— o - cean of mer - cy and peace.—
bound-less in love,— ful - ness of hea - ven on earth.—

1.

2.

2nd time D.C.
4th time fine

And it's —

54 In Christ alone

Words: Stuart Townend
Music: Keith Getty

Capo 1 (D)
Steadily

1. In Christ a-lone my hope is found, he is my light, my strength, my song; this cor-ner-stone, this so-lid ground, firm through the fier-cest drought and storm. What heights of love, what depths of
2. In Christ a-lone who took on flesh, ful-ness of God in help-less babe! This gift of love and right-eous-ness, scorned by the ones he came to save till on that cross as Je-sus
3. There in the ground his bo-dy lay, light of the world by dark-ness slain then burst-ing forth in glo-rious day up from the grave he rose a-gain! And as he stands in vic-to-
4. No guilt in life, no fear in death, this is the pow'r of Christ in me; from life's first cry to fi-nal breath, Je-sus com-mands my des-ti-ny. No pow'r of hell, no scheme of

Suggested guitar groove 'H' (see page 125)
This song is recorded on the Spring Harvest 2001 Live Worship Album & on the double album Celebrating 25 Years of Spring Harvest

120

peace, when fears are stilled, when striv - ings cease! My com - for-
died, the wrath of God was sa - tis - fied - for e - v'ry
ry sin's curse has lost its grip on me, for I am
man, can e - ver pluck me from his hand; till he re -

ter, my all in all, here in the love of Christ I stand.
sin on him was laid; here in the death of Christ I live.
his and he is mine - bought with the pre - cious blood of Christ.
turns or calls me home, here in the pow'r of Christ I'll stand!

55

In you we live

Steadily

Graham Kendrick
Arr. R. Lewis

In you— we live, Je-sus, in you— we move.

In you— we breathe, Je-sus, in you— we love. And we are

your bo-dy here, we are your bo-dy here.

(continued over...)

123

55a Breaking of the Bread

Agnus Dei

Jesus, Lamb of God,
have mercy on us.

Jesus, bearer of our sins,
have mercy on us.

Jesus, redeemer of the world,
grant us peace.

From Common Worship: Services and Prayers for the Church of England. Copyright © The Archbishops' Council 2000

Guitar Grooves 2

The practice steps here and on page 115 should be seen as just that. Take them one at a time and build confidence over days and weeks, regularly reviewing each step. Start with the eighth note grooves first before attempting the sixteenth note grooves as they are harder. If you are still struggling to read the grooves, find someone who can read music that could tap out the rhythm for you.

The following rhythm is one of the key strumming patterns in worship songs. It may look complicated, but if you have practiced the previous 6 steps you now have all the tools you need. Be careful to start each new groove back at 65 bpm and then gradually build the speed up.

Practice Step	Groove breakdown
1. Here is the groove in standard notation form	
2. Now here it is split into four separate beats each of which can be practiced separately	
3. Now begin to build the rhythm back up by practicing in pairs	
4. Once you can play each pair confidently (tap your foot as well!), put them together to give the full groove. Now apply this groove to song No 40 'He is the Lord' or No 61 'I will worship' to hear it in action	

Now that you know how to build up a strumming pattern, here are a few more to practice. If you look through the songs in this book, you'll find that many of them have one or more of these rhythms suggested at the bottom of the page.

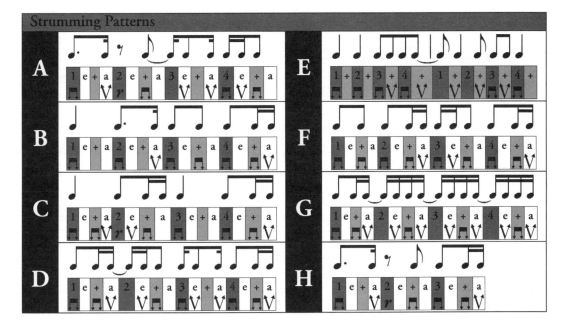

Richard Stephenson & Andy Flannagan

Please see the CD-ROM section of Spring Harvest Distinctive Sounds album and the Academy of Music Ministry's website at www.nexustrust.co.uk for details of more material relating to developing these skills.

56 It's a good thing

Disco feel

Bonnie Deuschle
& Andrew Baird

Chorus

It's a good thing— giv-ing thanks to God,— sing-ing prai-ses— to his

name. It's a good thing— giv-ing thanks to God:— ev-'ry one pro-claim

Last time to Coda

3rd time to bridge

it's a good thing.—
(It's a)

Verse

He shines lov-ing kind-ness in the morn-ing. He shines faith-

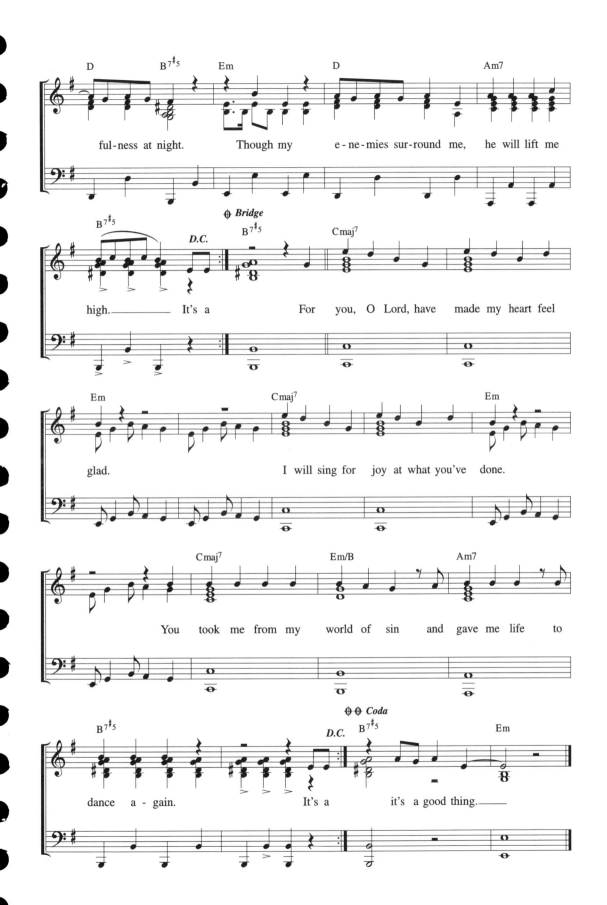

57
It's amazing

Exuberantly

Geraldine Latty

It's a-maz - ing,— a-stound-ing— ex - tra - va - gant grace. It's a-maz-
-ing, a-stound-ing— ex - tra-va - gant grace. It's a-maz - ing,— a-stound-ing— ex -
tra - va - gant grace. Lord to— you I lift my— praise. It's a-maz-
(Lord to— you we lift our)—

praise.

1. In all— my griev - ing and in all— my weep - ing your
2. In all— my pain— and through all— my dark - ness your
3. In all— my days— of qui - et— re - stor - ing your

grace still flows,— your grace still flows.— In all— my seek - ing and
grace still flows,— your grace still flows.— In my— in - dif - fer-ence and
grace still flows,— your grace still flows.— And when— I walk— with

Mid section

on my— re - turn - ing your grace still flows to me.— It's a-maz - praise.
through all— my hard - ness your grace still flows to me.—
joy o - ver-flow - ing your grace still flows to me.—

Thank-you for— your kind - ness that leads me to— re - pen - tance,—

thank you for— your power— that saves me, Je-sus! Thank you for— your name— that

lifts me to— the Fa - ther. What an— a-maz-ing,— ex - tra-va - gant grace! it's a-ma -

58 I will bless the Lord forever
(Made me glad)

Capo 3(D)

Miriam Webster

Worshipfully

1. I will bless the Lord for-e-ver,
   He has de-li-vered me from all fear,
2. Whom have I in hea-ven but you?

I will trust him at all times.
he has
There's none

set my feet up-on a rock.
I de-sire be-sides you.

And
And

I will not be moved, and I'll say of the Lord:
you have made me glad, and I'll say of the Lord:

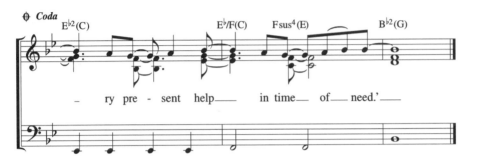

ry pre - sent help___ in time___ of ___ need.' ___

58a Praise the Lord!

Psalm 34: 1–4

I will extol the Lord at all times;
    his praise will always be on my lips.
My soul will boast in the Lord;
    let the afflicted hear and rejoice.
Glorify the Lord with me;
    let us exalt his name together.

I sought the Lord, and he answered me;
    he delivered me from all my fears.

59 I will glorify your name

Noel Robinson

Building

I will glo - ri - fy___ your name,___ glo - ri - fy___ your name,
mag - ni - fy___ your name,___ mag - ni - fy___ your name,

Last time to Coda

1.
— I will glo - ri - ry___ your name___ in all___ the earth.
— I will mag - ni - fy___ your name.

2.
— I will ___ in all___ the earth.___ I will

Coda

mag - ni - fy___ your name___ in all___ the earth,___ I will

mag - ni - fy___ your name___ in all___ the earth.

60 I will offer up my life

Gently

Matt Redman

1. I will of-fer up my life in spi-rit and truth,
2. You de-serve my ev-'ry breath for you've paid the great cost;

— pour-ing out the oil of love as my wor-ship to you.
— giv-ing up your life to death, e-ven death on a cross.

— In sur-ren-der I must give my ev-ery part;
— You took all my shame a-way, there de-fea-ted my sin,

— Lord, re-ceive the sac-ri-fice of a bro-ken heart.
— o-pened up the gates of heaven, and have bec-koned me in.

Suggested guitar groove 'C' (see page 125)
This song is recorded on the double album Celebrating 25 Years of Spring Harvest

Je-sus, what can I give,—— what can I bring—— to so faith-ful a friend,—

—to so lov-ing a King?—— Sav-iour, what can be said,—— what can be sung—

—as a praise of your name—— for the things you have done?——

—Oh, my words could not tell,—— not ev-en in part,—— of the

debt of love that is owed—— by this thank-ful heart.

61
I will worship
(You are worthy of my praise)

Worshipfully, with strength

David Ruis

Suggested guitar groove 'A' (see page 125)

all my— wor-ship, I will give— you all my— praise.———

— You a-lone— I long to— wor-ship, you a-lone— are

wor - thy— of— my— praise.———

61a Fixing our eyes on Jesus

Hebrews 12: 2

Let us fix our eyes on Jesus, the author and perfector of our faith,
who for the joy set before him endured the cross, scorning its shame,
and sat down at the right hand of the throne of God.

62   Jesus, be the centre

Moderately

Michael Frye

son that I live,___ Je - sus,___ Je - sus.___

62a Walking with Jesus

Let the meaning of the scriptures dawn upon our doubting hearts.
And may our spirits burn within us.

Let the joy of your resurrected presence thrill our fearful hearts
and may our spirits burn within us.

Let the bread of life for ever fill our hungry hearts
and may we always be satisfied.

In Jesus Christ our Lord,
Amen.

63 Jesus, all for Jesus

Steadily

Jennifer Atkinson
& Robin Mark

1. Je - sus, all for Je - sus; all I
2. All of my am - bi - tions hopes and plans I sur -

am and have and ev - er hope to be.
ren - der these in - to your hands.

be. hands. For it's

on - ly in your will that I am free. For it's

on - ly in your will that I am free.

Suggested guitar groove 'A' (see page 125)
This song is recorded on the double album Celebrating 25 Years of Spring Harvest

64

Jesus Christ is waiting

NOËL NOUVELET

Words: John L. Bell & Graham Maule
Music: French Trad.
Arr. David Ball

1. Je - sus Christ is wait - ing, wait-ing __ in the streets;
2. Je - sus Christ is rag - ing, rag-ing __ in the streets,
3. Je - sus Christ is heal - ing, heal-ing __ in the streets,
4. Je - sus Christ is danc - ing, danc-ing __ in the streets,
5. Je - sus Christ is call - ing, call-ing __ in the streets,

no one is his neigh - bour, all a - lone he eats.
where in - just - ice spi - rals and real __ hope re - treats.
cur - ing those who suf - fer, touch - ing __ those he greets.
where each sign of ha - tred he, with love, de - feats.
'Who will join my jour - ney? I will __ guide their feet.'

Lis - ten, Lord Je - sus, I am lone - ly too:
Lis - ten, Lord Je - sus, I am an - gry too:
Lis - ten, Lord Je - sus, I have pi - ty too:
Lis - ten, Lord Je - sus, I should tri - umph too;
Lis - ten, Lord Je - sus, let my fears be few:

make me, friend or stran - ger, fit to __ wait on you.
in the king - dom's cau - ses let me __ rage with you.
let my care be ac - tive, heal - ing __ just like you.
where good con - quers e - vil let me __ dance with you.
walk one step be - fore me; I will __ fol - low you.

65

Jesus Christ
(Once again)

Capo 1(D)

Matt Redman

Thoughtfully, not too fast

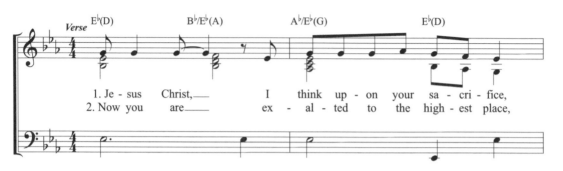

1. Je - sus Christ,___ I think up - on your sa - cri - fice,
2. Now you are___ ex - al - ted to the high - est place,

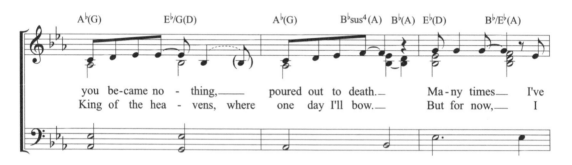

you be - came no - thing,___ poured out to death. Ma - ny times___ I've
King of the hea - vens, where one day I'll bow.___ But for now,___ I

won - dered at your gift of life, and I'm in that place___ once a - gain.
mar - vel at this sav - ing grace, and I'm full of praise___ once a - gain.

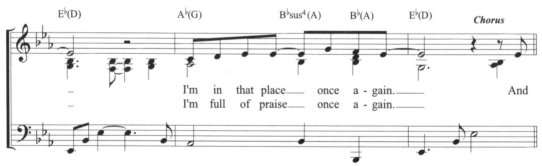

I'm in that place___ once a - gain.___ And
I'm full of praise___ once a - gain.___

Suggested guitar groove 'C' (see page 125)
This song is recorded on the Spring Harvest 20 Years Double Album

once a-gain I look up-on the cross where you died,— I'm

hum-bled by your mer-cy and I'm bro-ken in-side.— Once a-gain I thank you,

once a-gain I pour out my life.——— Thank you for the cross,

thank you for the cross, thank you for the cross, my friend.

friend. And

66 Jesus Christ, Holy One

Brightly

Nathan Fellingham

Je-sus Christ,___ Ho-ly One,___ the lif-ter of___ our heads,___

through you I come,___ con-qu'ring Son,___ to my Fa - ther___ in heav'n.___

_ And I'm con - fi-dent___ that I be-long to you,___ as the Spi-

rit tes-ti-fies.___ I shall___ not fear,___

fear has___ no hold,___ so I cry___ 'Ab-ba Fa - ther!'

Suggested guitar groove 'E' (see page 125)

67 Jesus draw me ever nearer
(May this journey)

Margaret Becker
& Keith Getty

Capo 1(D)
With feeling

1. Je-sus,— draw me e-ver near-er, as I
guide me through the tem-pest, keep my
trea-sures of the tri-al form with-

la-bour through the storm. You have called me to this
spi-rit staid and sure. When the mid-night meets the
in me as I go. And at the end of this long

pas-sage, and I'll fol-low though I'm worn. May this jour-ney bring a
morn-ing, let me love you e-ven more.
pas-sage, let me leave them at your throne.

bless-ing, may I rise—— on wings of faith: and at the— end of my heart's

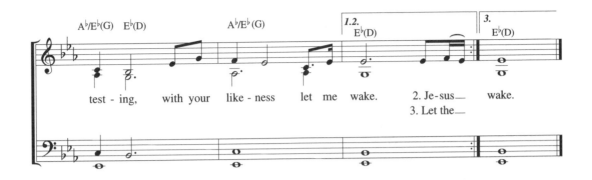

test - ing, with your like - ness let me wake. 2. Je-sus___ wake.
3. Let the___

67a Psalm 96 (Responsive)

Sing to the Lord a new song:
sing to the Lord, all the earth.
I will sing to the Lord.

Sing to the Lord, praise his name;
proclaim his salvation day after day.
I will sing to the Lord.

Declare his glory among the nations,
his marvellous deeds among all peoples.
I will sing to the Lord.

Great is the Lord and most worthy of praise;
he is to be feared above all gods.
I will sing to the Lord.

Let all creation sing for joy,
sing for joy for he comes.
I will sing to the Lord.

He will judge the world in righteousness
and the peoples with his truth.
I will sing to the Lord.

68 Jesus, hope of the nations
(Hope of the nations)

Strong rhythm

Brian Doerksen

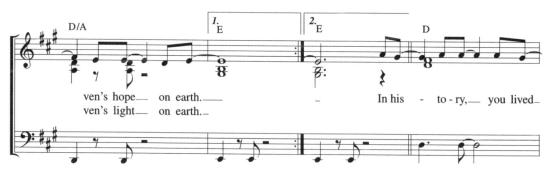

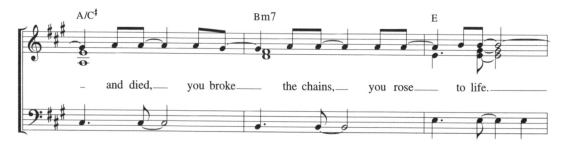

69. Jesus is Lord

Majestically

Stuart Townend
& Keith Getty

1. 'Je-sus is Lord' – the cry that e-choes through cre-a-tion:
   re-splen-dent power, e-ter-nal Word, our rock. The Son of
   God, the King whose glo-ry fills the hea-vens, yet bids us
   come to taste this liv-ing bread.

2. Je-sus is Lord – whose word su-stains the stars and pla-nets,
   yet in his wis-dom, laid a-side his crown. Je-sus the
   man, who washed our feet, who bore our suf-fering, be-came a
   curse to bring sal-va-tion's plan.

3. Je-sus is Lord – the tomb is glo-ri-ous-ly emp-ty!
   Not e-ven death could crush this King of love! The price is
   paid, the chains are loosed, and we're for-gi-ven, and we can
   run in-to the arms of God.

4. 'Je-sus is Lord' – a shout of joy, a cry of an-guish,
   as he re-turns, and e-very knee bows low. Then e-very
   eye and e-very heart will see his glo-ry, the Judge of
   all will take his chil-dren home.

Bridges to D

70 Jesus, the source

Graham Kendrick

1. Je - sus, the source of all our joy, full of truth and
God who none has e - ver seen, you have brought so
can we e - ver com - pre - hend all your blood has
hear the pas - sion of your prayer that we may be

grace. The Fa - ther's liv - ing, breath - ing Word,_____ what more could I
near the beat - ing heart of love di - vine_____ close e - nough to
bought, mak - ing a way for us to share the ve - ry life of
one, so all the world_____ may be - lieve_____ you have tru - ly

say? Pour out the pas - sion of your heart that sent you from_____ a -
hear. And in your words we hear a voice that puts our fear_____ to
God. To know the love that burned for you be - fore the world_____ be -
come. Teach us to love with that same love that sent you from_____ a -

Last time to Coda ⊕

bove, to_____ know the Fa - ther_____ and make known his a - maz - ing
flight: the Fa - ther sing - ing_____ o - ver us songs of pure_____ de -
gan, and_____ by your po - wer_____ to be - come God's own chil - _____
bove to_____ know the Fa - ther_____ and make known

153

71 Jesus you alone

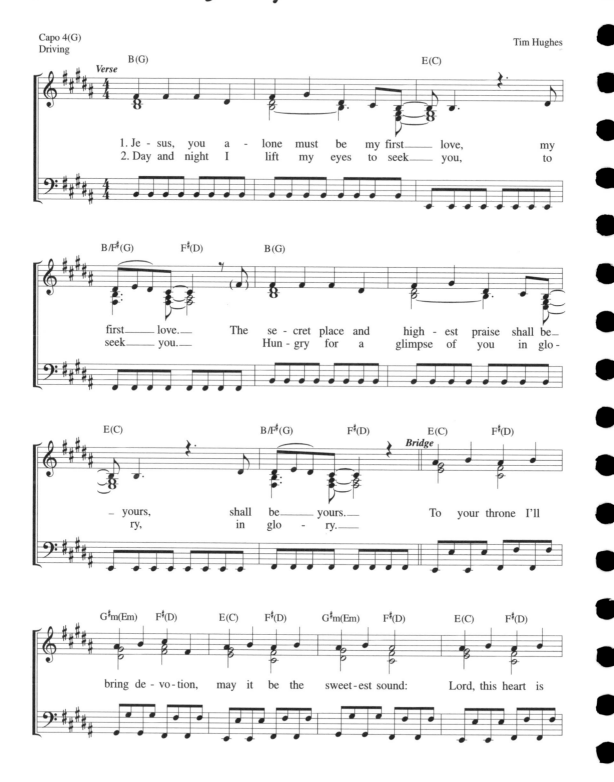

Capo 4(G)
Driving

Tim Hughes

1. Je - sus, you a - lone must be my first___ love, my
2. Day and night I lift my eyes to seek___ you, to

first___ love. The se - cret place and high - est praise shall be___
seek___ you.___ Hun - gry for a glimpse of you in glo -

___ yours, shall be___ yours. To your throne I'll
ry, in glo - ry.___

bring de - vo - tion, may it be the sweet-est sound: Lord, this heart is

Suggested guitar groove 'F' (see page 125)

reach - ing for you now.

Chorus

So I'll set my sights up - on you,
set my life up - on
You a - lone will be my pas - sion,
Je - sus, you will be

your praise;
ne - ver look - ing to a - no - ther way.
my song:
you will find me long -

ing af - ter you.

D.C. (Last time D.S.) | To end

72

King of the ages

Rehearsal Tips

It's often amazed me as I travel how something as fundamental as rehearsals get overlooked within worship teams! Even when songs have been introduced it's always good to work on some arrangements to enhance the sound and ultimately aid the church in its worship. The Bible encourages us to make a joyful sound to the Lord not a woeful one, so lets look at some aspects which might help us in our rehearsing together.

- If you are responsible for the rehearsal, give the time you want everyone to arrive and make sure this includes set up time e.g. 7.30 for 7.45 pm.
- Come with some songs in mind to rehearse or introduce. It's a good habit to start with thanking the team for turning up, ask how everyone is generally and then pray!
- Let the team know what time you hope to finish by, generally a two hour rehearsal midweek is adequate. If you have a persistent latecomer quietly take them aside and explain to them their lateness is affecting the entire team. Often there are genuine reasons which are understandable and maybe a solution can be found between you.
- Ask everyone to switch off mobile phones, they can be very distracting.
- Don't overload your rehearsals – too many songs mean they probably won't remember by Sunday!
- Ask your team to have the latest songbook you are teaching from; providing you aren't expecting a new book each month it looks tidier than endless pieces of paper.
- Mic the vocalists up! There is nothing more frustrating than singers trying to hear themselves over instruments that are too loud. Levels don't need to be set for main stage Wembley so encourage everyone to turn down and play at reasonable levels.
- Get players to listen to each other, allowing different sounds to be heard throughout the song and giving space to the melodic instruments especially during the quieter songs.
- Look at the way you begin and end songs, vary how you do this and see if you can put one or two together occasionally.
- Consider whether one of your capable vocalists could sing the song once through before others join in. Block vocal singing can sound monotonous.
- As musicians we are a sensitive bunch. Jokey comments about someone's playing, or impatience if someone can't get a chord sequence, can quickly become hurtful and offend. Remember to encourage more than correct.

Finally worship together! Don't allow the rehearsal to become a means to an end, Let a song flow and enjoy making good music together.

Trish Morgan

73
Lamp unto my feet
(It is you)

Steadily

Darlene Zschech

74   Let everything that has breath

Matt Redman

Let ev-ery-thing that, ev-ery-thing that, ev-ery-thing that

has breath, praise the Lord. Let ev-ery-thing that, ev-ery-thing that,

Last time to Coda

ev-ery-thing that has breath praise the Lord.

Verse

1. Praise___ you in the morn - ing,___
2. Praise___ you in the hea - vens,___

praise___ you in the ev - ening,___   praise___ you when I'm young and when I'm old.__
join - ing with the an - gels,___   prais - ing you for - e - ver and a day.__

Suggested guitar groove 'D' (see page 125)
This song is recorded on the double album Celebrating 25 Years of Spring Harvest

Praise___ you when I'm laugh - ing,___
Praise___ you on the earth now,___

praise___ you when I'm griev - ing,___
join - ing with cre - a - tion,___

praise___ you ev-ery sea - son of the soul.___
call - ing all the na - tions to your praise.___

If we could see how much you're worth your
If they could see how much you're worth your

power, your might, your end-less love, then sure - ly we would ne - ver cease to
they

praise.___

has breath, praise the Lord.___

rall . . . .

⊕ Coda

75

Let us bow

Capo 3(D)

Ian White

♩ = 68

1. Let us bow be-fore the my-ste-ry____ of God. Let us
2. Let us bow be-fore the my-ste-ry____ of God, and for-

li-sten for he calls us each by name. Let us rest here in a cli-mate of__ com-
gi-ven re - learn now to for - give. Let us rest here in a cli-mate of__ com-

pas - sion,__ and let his heal-ing, and let his heal-ing, and
pas - sion,__ and let for - give-ness, his deep for - give-ness, and

let his heal-ing be-gin____ a - gain.
let for - give-ness be-gin____ to live.

Light of my life

Chris Bowater

Light of my life, love of my heart, be Lord in ev-'ry-thing;— light of my life, love of my heart, be Lord in ev-'ry-thing;— ho-ly, right-eous, migh-ty, pow'r-ful and pure.—

Light of my Lord in ev-'ry-thing,— be Lord in ev-'ry-thing.—

77

Light of the world
(Here I am to worship)

Gradually building

Tim Hughes

Verse

1. Light of the world, you stepped down in-to dark - ness,
2. King of all days, oh so high - ly ex - al - ted,

o - pened my eyes, let me see. Beau - ty that made this
glo - rious in hea - ven a - bove, hum - bly you came to the

heart a - dore you, hope of a life spent with you.
earth you cre - a - ted, all for love's sake be - came poor.

Chorus

So here I am to wor - ship, here I am to bow down, here I am to

say that you're my God: you're al - to - ge - ther love - ly, al - to - ge - ther

Suggested guitar groove 'B' or 'C' (see page 125)
This song is recorded on the Spring Harvest 2002 Live Worship Album, the 2001 Praise Mix Album
& on the double album Celebrating 25 Years of Spring Harvest

78

Lord, I'm grateful
(Grace)

With energy

Stuart Townend
& Fred J Heumann

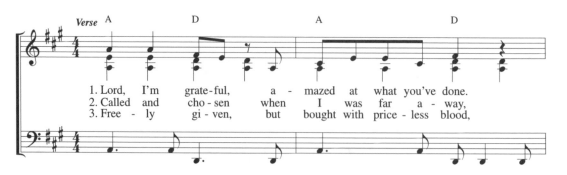

1. Lord, I'm grate-ful, a - mazed at what you've done.
2. Called and cho - sen when I was far a - way,
3. Free - ly giv - en, but bought with price - less blood,

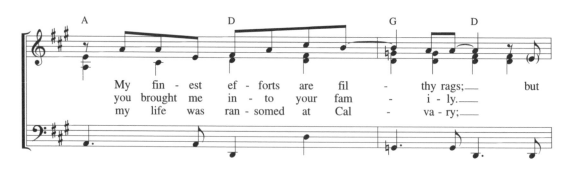

My fin - est ef - forts are fil - thy rags;— but
you brought me in - to your fam - i - ly.—
my life was ran - somed at Cal - va - ry;—

I'm made righ - teous by trust - ing in the Son—
Free, for - gi - ven, my guilt is washed a - way;
there my Je - sus gave e - v'ry - thing he could

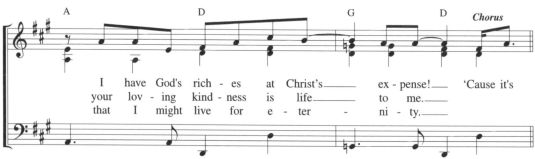

I have God's rich - es at Christ's ex - pense!— 'Cause it's
your lov - ing kind - ness is life to me.—
that I might live for e - ter - ni - ty.—

167

79

Lord the love you give
(Let my life be like a love song)

♩ = 68

Tom Slater
& Brenton Brown

80   Lord, you've been good to me

Graham Kendrick

1. Lord, you've been good to me all my life, all my life;
your lov-ing kind - ness ne - ver fails.
I will re-mem-ber all you have done,
bring from my heart thanks-giv-ing songs.

2. So may each breath I take be for you, Lord,
on - ly you, giv-ing you back the life I owe.
Love so a - maz-ing, mer-cy so free.
Lord, you've been good, so good to me.

This song is recorded on the Spring Harvest 2002 Live Worship Album

New ev-'ry morn - ing is— your love,

filled with com-pas - sion from— a-bove.—

Grace and for-give - ness full— and free,

Lord, you've—been good to— me.

81   May the words of my mouth

Tim Hughes
& Rob Hill

Steadily

1. May the

Verse

words   of my mouth,   and the   thoughts___ of my heart   bless your

you   be my vi - sion, Lord, will   you___ be my guide?   Be my

name, bless your___ name,   Je - sus.   And the   deeds   of the day,   and the

hope,   be my___ light   and the way.   And I'll   look   not for ri - ches, nor

truth   in my ways speak of   you,   speak of___ you,   Je - sus.   For this___ is what___

prais - es on earth,   on - ly   you'll   be   the first of   my___ heart.

Chorus

___   I'm glad___ to do,___   it's time___ to live___ a life___ of love___ that plea - ses you.

Suggested guitar groove 'B' or 'C' (see page 125)
This song is recorded on the Spring Harvest 2002 New Songs Album

82 May your love be upon us

Capo 3(D)

Joanne Boyce
& Mike Stanley

With conviction

res - cue__ their souls_____ from death; to

love be up - on us, O Lord,_____ as we

F(D)   C/E(A/C♯)   Dm(Bm)   Dm/C(Bm/A)

Lord loves jus - tice and right_____ and

keep them a - live,__ keep them a - live.__ May your

D.C.

place all our hope__ in__ you.__ May your

D.C.

Gm⁷(Em⁷)   C(A)   *D.C.*

fills the earth with his love._____ May your

Coda ⊕ F(D)

83 Minute by minute

84

Multiply your love

Andy Park

♩ = 92

Verse E

1. Mul-ti-ply— your   love   through us   to the lost and— the
   love   through me   to some-one— in
   church   through us   to the ends of— the

C♯m7

least;   let us be— your heal-ing hands,
need,   help me, Lord,— to free-ly give
earth;   where there's on-ly bar-ren-ness

Bsus4

your in-stru-ments— of— peace.   May our sin-gle
this grace that I've— re-ceived.   Let my sin-gle
let us see— new— birth.   Use us as your

A   C♯m7

pur-pose be   to i-mi-tate—your— life,   through our sim-ple
pur-pose be   to i-mi-tate—your— life,   through my sim-ple
la-bou-rers,   work-ing side— by— side,   let us see your

(continued over...)

Bridges to E

From G

From A

From C

From D

85

My heart is captivated
(Divine exchange)

Lara Martin

Gently

My heart is cap - ti - va - ted, Lord, by you a - lone;

cap - tured by the awe - some-ness of you a - lone.

Melt-ed by the grace and mer - cy you have shown, I stand in won - der.

I reach to you, the one who makes the blind eyes see, who breaks

(continued over...)

the chains— of sick-ness with— au-tho - ri-ty.— Re-stor - ing what— was bro-ken,— so it may fly a-gain.— I live— to wor - ship you;— I breathe— to wor - ship you.— All of— my days— your face I— will seek.— For as— I wor - ship you, you lead— me to— that place,— to— that place of di - vine ex -

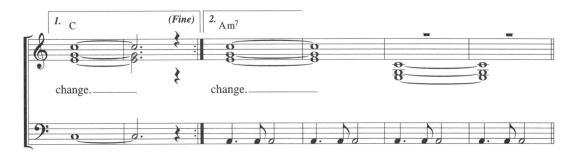

change.   change.

Je - sus,   Je - sus.   Je - sus,

Je - sus.

85a Prayer for the Mission of the Church

Almighty God,
who called your Church to witness
that in Christ you were reconciling the world to yourself:
help us so to proclaim the good news of your love,
that all who hear it may be reconciled to you
through him who died for us and rose again
and reigns with you in the unity of the Holy Spirit,
one God, now and for ever.
Amen.

86 Nearer my God to thee

Words: Sarah Flower Adams
Music: Lowell Mason

87 O for a heart to praise my God

Words: Charles Wesley (1707-88)
Music: Simon Goodall

1. O for a heart to praise my God, a heart from sin set
   hum - ble, low - ly con - trite heart, be - liev - ing, true and

free; a heart that's sprin - kled with the blood so
clean, which nei - ther life nor death can part from

free - ly shed for me. A heart re - signed, sub -
him that dwells with - in. A heart re - newed in

mis - sive, meek. My great Re - deem - er's throne where
ev - 'ry thought and full of love di -

(continued over...)

This song is recorded on the Spring Harvest 2003 New Songs Album

on - ly Christ is heard to speak, where Je - sus reigns a - lone. 2. A

2. - vine;_____ per - fect_ and_ right_ and pure and good,_____ a

co - py Lord, of thine._____

Thy na - ture,_ gra - cious Lord im - part,_ come quick - ly_ from_ a - bove_____ and

87a Prayer to lead others into freedom

Father God, you saw a tribe of slaves and made them into a nation in whom you could entrust your law, your mission and your Son.

Continue to work in us, that we may lead those who are enslaved in sin into your freedom and plan that they too may reflect your holiness, your mission and your salvation.

Amen.

88 O God, maker of the earth and heaven
(Hear our prayers)

Keith Getty
& Jason Mandryk

Quietly rhythmic

1. O God, ma-ker of the earth and hea-ven, gi-ven
2. Fa-ther, look up-on your trou-bled chil-dren, save them
3. Guard them when they suf-fer per-se-cu-tion, grant them

to a world in need. Act now in your pow-er
in their dark-est hour. Streng-then them to speak your
the grace to stand faith-ful un-to their

to de-li-ver. O Lord God, hear our prayers.
name with cou-rage. O Lord God, hear our prayers.
tes-ti-mo-ny. O Lord God, hear our prayers.

Chorus

Oh, make known to all that you're

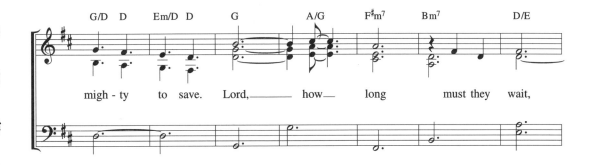

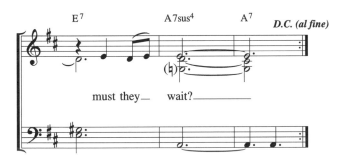

migh-ty to save. Lord,_____ how_____ long must they wait,

must they_____ wait?_____

88a Prayer before communion

Most merciful Lord,
your love compels us to come in.
Our hands were unclean,
our hearts were unprepared;
we were not fit
even to eat the crumbs from under your table.
But you, Lord, are the God of our salvation,
and share your bread with sinners.
So cleanse and feed us
with the precious body and blood of your Son,
that he may live in us and we in him;
and that we, with the whole company of Christ,
may sit and eat in your kingdom.
Amen.

89 O God of burning cleansing flame
(Send the fire!)

Music: Lex Loizides
Words: William Booth (1829-1912)
Adpt. Lex Loizides

Steadily

1. O God of burn-ing, clean-sing flame: send the fi – re! Your
2. God of E-li-jah, hear our cry: send the fi – re! And
3. It's fire we want, for fire we plead: send the fi – re! The
4. To make our weak hearts strong and brave: send the fi – re! To

blood-bought gift to-day we—claim: send the fire to-day! Look
make us fit to live or— die: send the fire to-day! To
fire will meet our e-very—need: send the fire to-day! For
live, a dy-ing world to—save: send the fire to-day! Oh,

down and see this wait-ing host, and send the prom-ised Ho-ly Ghost; we
burn up e-very trace of sin, to bring the light and glo-ry in, the
strength to al-ways do what's right, for grace to con-quer in the fight, for
see us on your al-tar lay, we give our lives to you to-day, so

Suggested guitar groove 'F' (see page 125)

need a - no - ther Pen - te - cost! Send the fire to - day!
re - vo - lu - tion now be - gin! Send the fire to - day!
power to walk the world in___ white: send the fire to - day!
crown the of - f'ring now we___ pray: send the fire to - day!

To repeat

Last time only

rall . . . .

Send the fire to - day!
Send the fire to - day!
Send the fire to - day!
Send the fire to -

- day! Send the fire to-

day!

90 Oh kneel me down again
(Humble King)

Brenton Brown

Suggested guitar groove 'F' (see page 125)

91 O Lord my God!
(How great thou art)

HOW GREAT THOU ART

Stuart K. Hine

Majestically

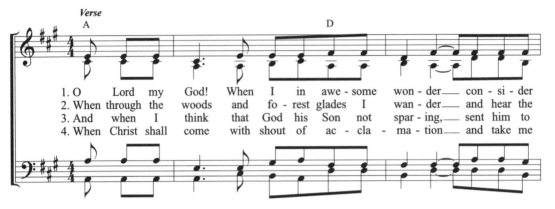

1. O Lord my God! When I in awe-some won-der ___ con-si-der
2. When through the woods and fo-rest glades I wan-der ___ and hear the
3. And when I think that God his Son not spar-ing, ___ sent him to
4. When Christ shall come with shout of ac-cla-ma-tion ___ and take me

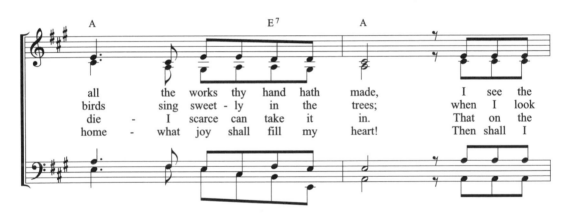

all   the works thy hand hath made,   I see the
birds   sing sweet-ly in the trees;   when I look
die - I scarce can take it in.   That on the
home - what joy shall fill my heart!   Then shall I

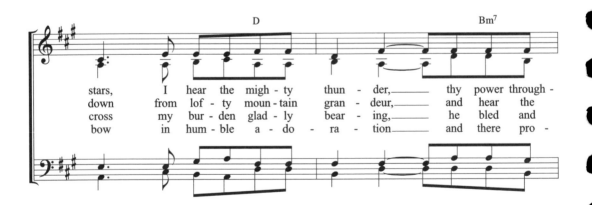

stars,   I hear the migh-ty thun - der, ___ thy power through-
down   from lof-ty moun-tain gran-deur, ___ and hear the
cross   my bur-den glad-ly bear-ing, ___ he bled and
bow   in hum-ble a-do-ra-tion ___ and there pro-

out   the un - i - verse dis - played: Then sings my   soul, my Sav-iour God to
brook, and feel the gen - tle   breeze;
died   to take a - way   my   sin:
claim, my God, how great thou   art!

thee,   how great thou art!   How great thou art!   Then sings my

soul, my Sav-iour God, to thee,   how great thou art! How great thou art!

Alternative ending

thee,————————————— how great thou art!   How great thou art!

92

O my soul
(Like eagles)

Capo 3(D)

Kevin Dukes
& Marsha Skidmore

♩ = 112

O my soul,— do you not know,— have you not heard?—

— It's been told— from the be-gin-ning, the

Lord, your God,— is on your side. O my soul,— don't be a-fraid,—

— hope in the Lord;— by his righ-teous-ness— and pow-

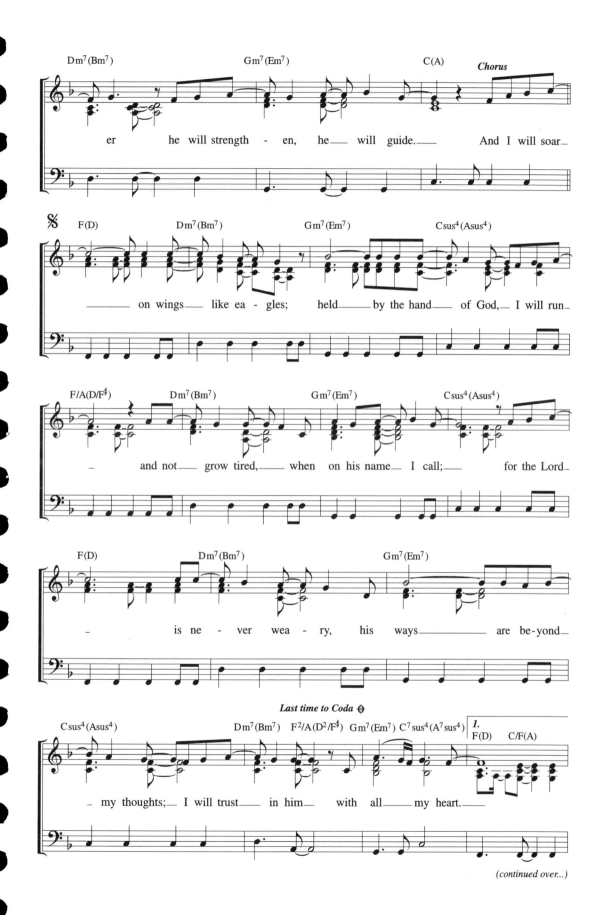

(continued over...)

Arranging a worship song

An arrangement can either enhance a song or cause a distraction to the worshippers! Cluttered arrangements (too much being played by the musicians) is as good as no arrangement at all! The style of music often dictates the tempo of the song, so make sure that the tempo is appropriate, then choose the musical style. If the song is too fast, it could prohibit the worshippers reflecting on the very words they are singing. Not all styles will suit a song!

A good arrangement must have a good format. e.g. Intro, Verse 1, Verse 2, Chorus, Mid-Intro, Verse 3, Chorus, Chorus and Outro.

- The intro could be the last line or the first line of the song. It could also be a fresh 4 or 8 bar melody. Make sure it is very obvious when the congregation should start singing.

- Verse 1 – Keep this fairly simple so that the congregation is not overwhelmed by the band. If the arrangement is a ballad such as 'Here I am to worship' (see no 77) you could leave out the drum kit and bass guitar. A percussion instrument is useful for keeping the band in time. Use solo instruments, at least to play the main melody – the most important part of the arrangement.

- Chorus 1 – The band can build dynamically, not giving away too much, otherwise the rest of the arrangement could be an anticlimax. This also gives the congregation an opportunity to learn the song, if new.

- Verse 2 – Add some extra melodic lines or counter melodies in this verse as an embellishment to the main melody. The drums and bass could enter this verse with the main groove – the general feel of the song. The bass and drum kit are the primary instruments that establish the groove.

- Chorus 2 – As the congregation may still be settling into the song, it is advisable to keep the arrangement on the second chorus the same as on the first chorus. Perhaps you could slightly increase the dynamics.

- Mid Intro (also known as a link) – This could be a variation on the intro or the intro played again. Why a mid-introduction? This could be the section of the arrangement where the band continues playing without the congregation singing, creating a musical foundation on top of which the worship leader can speak to the congregation, use some liturgy or read Scripture.

- Last Verse – Depending on the lyrics (important deciding factor) you could end the whole song with this final verse.

- Last Chorus – If this chorus will follow the last verse, the dynamics could be stronger. However, be flexible as the worship leader, during spontaneous worship, may want to transit immediately into another song. Many congregations appreciate a flow of one song to the next. The arrangements play an important part in aiding this flow. Both spontaneous and scripted worship has its place in the wider church setting.

- The Outro – Opposite of the Intro, could be the last line of the song repeated by the band only or the intro repeated for the last time. The Outro will probably conclude the song. Slowing down the tempo, depending on the style, can also be quite effective.

So, the importance of a good arrangement to a worship song is to enhance the song, not to draw attention to the band! Ultimately, as with every aspect of worship, everything must help us focus and point towards Jesus.

Steve A. Thompson, Beracah Music International

93 Oh yes, how I love Jesus

David Hind
& Malcolm W Baxter

Steady 2 feel, gradually building

1. Oh yes, how I love Je - sus,
2. Oh yes, how I love Je - sus,
3. Oh yes, how I love Je - sus,
4. Oh yes, how I love Je - sus,

friend of the lone - ly, heal - ing my
find - ing the lost, he shows them the
all who have wan - dered, lost and a -
hope for the hope - less, peace for the

pain. Down through the a - ges,
way. He makes the blind see,
lone; no con - dem - na - tion,
storm. All of my mourn - ing

he ne - ver chan - ges, oh, I love
he sets the bound free, when you love
just re - sto - ra - tion, those who love
he turns to dan - cing, Oh, I love

94

One heart, one Spirit

Dave Bilbrough

Steady 4

Chorus

One heart, one Spi - rit; we are called by God
to reach out and serve one an-o - ther in the Fa - ther's love.

Verse

1. We've star - ted a jour - ney and the
2. The way may be cost - ly,____ the

road may be long;___ we won't be dis-trac - ted till the work is all done.___
price will be great,___ we're go - ing the dis - tance,___ what e - ver it takes.___

95

Open the eyes of my heart

Simply

Paul Baloche

Suggested guitar groove 'D' (see page 125)

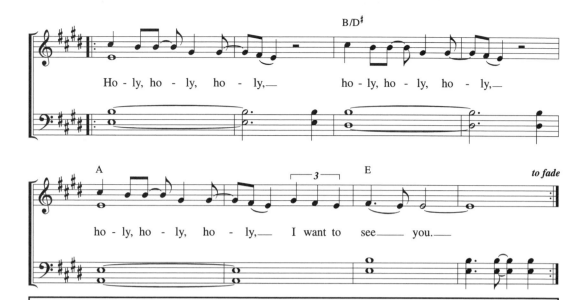

Ho - ly, ho - ly, ho - ly,— ho - ly, ho - ly, ho - ly,—

ho - ly, ho - ly, ho - ly,— I want to see— you.—

to fade

95a Moses and Jesus

From Hebrews 3

Brothers and sisters, we are holy partners in a heavenly calling.
Let us consider Jesus, the apostle and high priest of our confession
and be faithful to our calling, that we may enter God's rest.
(A brief silence may be kept)

Moses, God's servant, was faithful to the one who appointed him;
but Jesus is more faithful still.

Moses was a building;
Jesus is the builder.

Moses was worthy of honour;
Jesus is worthy of all honour.

Moses was a faithful servant in God's house;
Jesus was faithful as a Son over God's house.

Therefore, as the Holy Spirit says:
Today, if you hear his voice, do not harden your hearts
as people did long ago in the wilderness.

We are holy partners in a heavenly calling.
Let us consider Jesus, the apostle and high priest of our confession
and be faithful to our calling, that we may enter God's rest.

96 Opening our hearts to you
(Highest praise)

James Gregory

1. O-pen-ing our hearts to you,— fo-cus-ing our eyes on you,— lift-ing up our hands to you,— sing-ing out—this song for you;— prai-ses that will fill the skies,— rai-sing you o-ver our lives,— lift-ing up the Sa-viour high.—

2. You are so a-maz-ing Lord,— a beau-ti-ful and migh-ty God,— com-pas-sio-nate and mer-ci-ful,— glo-ri-ous—and po-wer-ful.— King o-ver the u-ni-verse,— won-der-f'ly in love with us,— pas-sio-nate a-bout the earth.—

Suggested guitar groove 'E' (see page 125)

We give— you the high - est praise,—

we give— you the high - est praise,—

96a Praise and glory to God

Revelation 7: 11 & 12

All the angels were standing around the throne and around the elders
and the four living creatures. They fell down on their faces before the
throne and worshipped God, saying:

> 'Amen!
> Praise and glory
> and wisdom and thanks and honour
> and power and strength
> be to our God for ever and ever.
> Amen!'

Our God is a great big God

With a 'Gospel' feel

Jo & Nigel Hemming

Our God— is a great big God, our God— is a great big God,—

our God— is a great big God and he holds us in his hands.—

He's high - er than a sky - scrap - er—— and he's

deep-er than a sub-ma-rine.—— He's wi-der than the u - ni-verse— and be-

98 Pierced

With gentle movement

Phil Hart
& Joanne Hogg

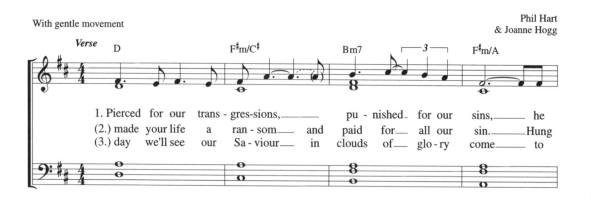

1. Pierced for our trans - gres-sions,_____ pu - nished_ for our sins,_____ he
(2.) made your life a ran - som__ and paid for_ all our sin.____Hung
(3.) day we'll see our Sa - viour_ in clouds of glo - ry come____ to

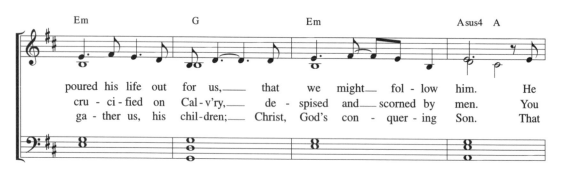

poured his life out for us,_____ that we might__ fol - low him. He
cru - ci - fied on Cal - v'ry,_____ de - spised and__ scorned by men. You
ga - ther us, his chil-dren;____ Christ, God's con - quer - ing Son. That

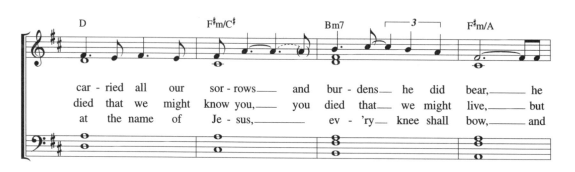

car - ried all our sor - rows____ and bur - dens__ he did bear,_____ he
died that we might know you,____ you died that__ we might live,_____ but
at the name of Je - sus,____ ev - 'ry__ knee shall bow,_____ and

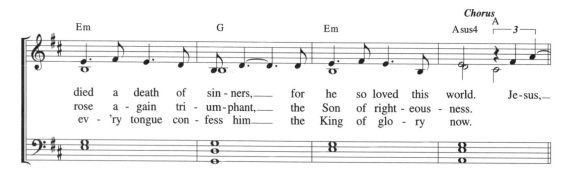

died a death of sin - ners,____ for he so loved this world. Je-sus,__
rose a - gain tri - um-phant,____ the Son of right - eous - ness.
ev - 'ry tongue con - fess him____ the King of glo - ry now.

This song is recorded on the Spring Harvest 2003 New Songs Album

99 Praise to Christ, the Lord incarnate

Words: Martin E. Leckebusch
Music & words adpt. Graham Kendrick

Steadily ♩ = 106

Verse

1. Praise to Christ, the Lord in - car - nate, gift of God by hu - man
   Christ, the Man of Sor - rows, tast - ing death for our re -
   Christ, the Priest e - ter - nal: still for us he in - ter -

birth: he it is who came a - mong us, shared our
lease: his the cup of bit - ter an - guish, ours the
cedes; still he sees our pains and prob - lems — how he

life and showed our worth; ours the tur - moil he en - coun - tered, ours the
par - don, ours the peace; his the blood that seals for - give - ness, ours the
un - der - stands our needs! Ye - ster - day, to - day, for - e - ver, al - ways

fight he made his own; ___ now with - in our hearts his
weight of guilt he bore — ___ so by death and re - sur -
he re - mains the same: ___ pledged to bring us to the

This song is recorded on the Spring Harvest 2002 New Songs Album

Spi - rit makes his way of free - dom known.
rec - tion Christ has o - pened hea - ven's door.
Fa - ther, strong in grace and free from blame.

Chorus

Praise to Christ our Sa - viour and our King.

Praise to Christ our King.

2. Praise to
3. Praise to

King.

King.

100 Praise my soul, the King of heaven

PRAISE MY SOUL
Capo 2(C)
Majestically

Music: John Goss (1800-80)
Words: Henry Francis Lyte (1793-1847)

1. Praise, my soul, the King of hea - ven; to his feet thy tri - bute bring. Ran - somed, healed, re - stored, for - given, who like thee his praise should sing? Praise him! Praise him! Praise him! Praise him! Praise the e - ver - last - ing King!
2. Praise him for his grace and fa - vour to our fa - thers in di - stress; praise him, still the same for - ever, slow to chide, and swift to bless. Praise him! Praise him! Praise him! Praise him! Glo - rious in his faith - ful - ness.
3. Fa - ther - like, he tends and spares us; well our fee - ble frame he knows; in his hands he gen - tly bears us, re - scues us from all our foes. Praise him! Praise him! Praise him! Praise him! Wide - ly as his mer - cy flows.
4. An - gels help us to a - dore him; ye be - hold him face to face; sun and moon, bow down be - fore him, dwel - lers all in time and space. Praise him! Praise him! Praise him! Praise him! Praise with us the God of grace!

101 Show me how to stand for justice

DIM OND JESU

Words: Martin E Leckebusch
Music Robert Lowry (1826-99)

Capo 1(G)

1. Show me how to stand for jus-tice:— how to work for what is
2. Teach my heart to trea-sure mer-cy, whe-ther gi-ven or re-
3. Glad-ly I em-brace a life-style mo-delled on your liv-ing

right, how to chal-lenge false as-sump-tions,— how to walk with-in the
ceived— for my need has not di-min-ished— since the day I first be-
word, in hu-mi-li-ty sub-mit-ting— to the truth which I have

light. May I learn to share more free-ly— in a world so full of
lieved: let me seek no sa-tis-fac-tion boast-ing of what I have
heard. Make me con-scious of your pre-sence— e-very day in all I

greed, show-ing your im-mense com-pas-sion— by the life I choose to lead.
done, but re-joice that I am par-doned— and ac-cep-ted in your Son.
do: by your Spi-rit's gra-cious prompt-ing— may I learn to walk with you.

102 Sovereign Lord

Martyn Layzell

1. So - v'reign Lord,— o - ver all,— you are reign-ing for-
2. Lord— of lords,— now— en-throned, who can stand in—your

e - ver. Wor - ship flows— from— our lips,—
pre - sence? Fire— of love,— Ho - ly One,—

we have come for just— one glimpse.— And we sing hal - le -
you burn brigh - ter than— the sun.—

lu - ia, hal - le - lu - ia, hal - le - lu -

ia.　　　Ma - je - sty,　reign — in — me,　your right —

— hand　en-fold - ing — me.　Earth — ap - plaud,　hea - vens —

— sing　at — the — sight　of Christ — the — King. —

King.　Ma - je - — King. —

103 Standing now before you
(Desire)

Steadily

Mark Tedder

Standing now before you I draw near,
open up my heart and let me hear.
Let me feel the warmth of your embrace,
let me see the pleasure reflected on your face. And I seek

104   Tender Saviour

Nick and Anita Haigh

in my — bro - ken - ness, —   ten-der Sa - viour.

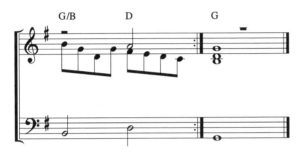

104a God's peace
John 14: 27

Peace I leave with you; my peace I give you.
I do not give to you as the world gives.
Do not let your hearts be troubled and do not be afraid.

105 Thank you heavenly Father
(Jesus in my house)

Judy Bailey

1. Thank you, hea-v'nly Fa-ther for your love for me.
2. Thank you for the pur-pose you have placed in me.

I'm for-e-ver grate-ful that you sa-cri-ficed your Son.
Thank you for for-give-ness and the chance to start a-gain.

You saved my soul and changed my de-sti-ny.
I face the fu-ture know-ing I will be

Thank you, God, for Je-sus in me. I'm so glad that
safe and sound with Je-sus in me.

Je - sus lives___ in my house.___ Good to know that he is here___ with me now.___

___ All of my life Je-sus in me, Je-sus in my house. All of my life

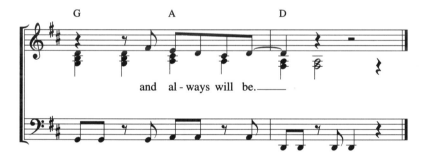

and al - ways will be.___

105a   **This is love**

1 John 4: 10

This is love: not that we loved God, but that he loved us and sent his
Son as an atoning sacrifice for our sins.

106 Thank you for the cross, Lord
(Worthy is the Lamb)

Darlene Zschech

Moderately

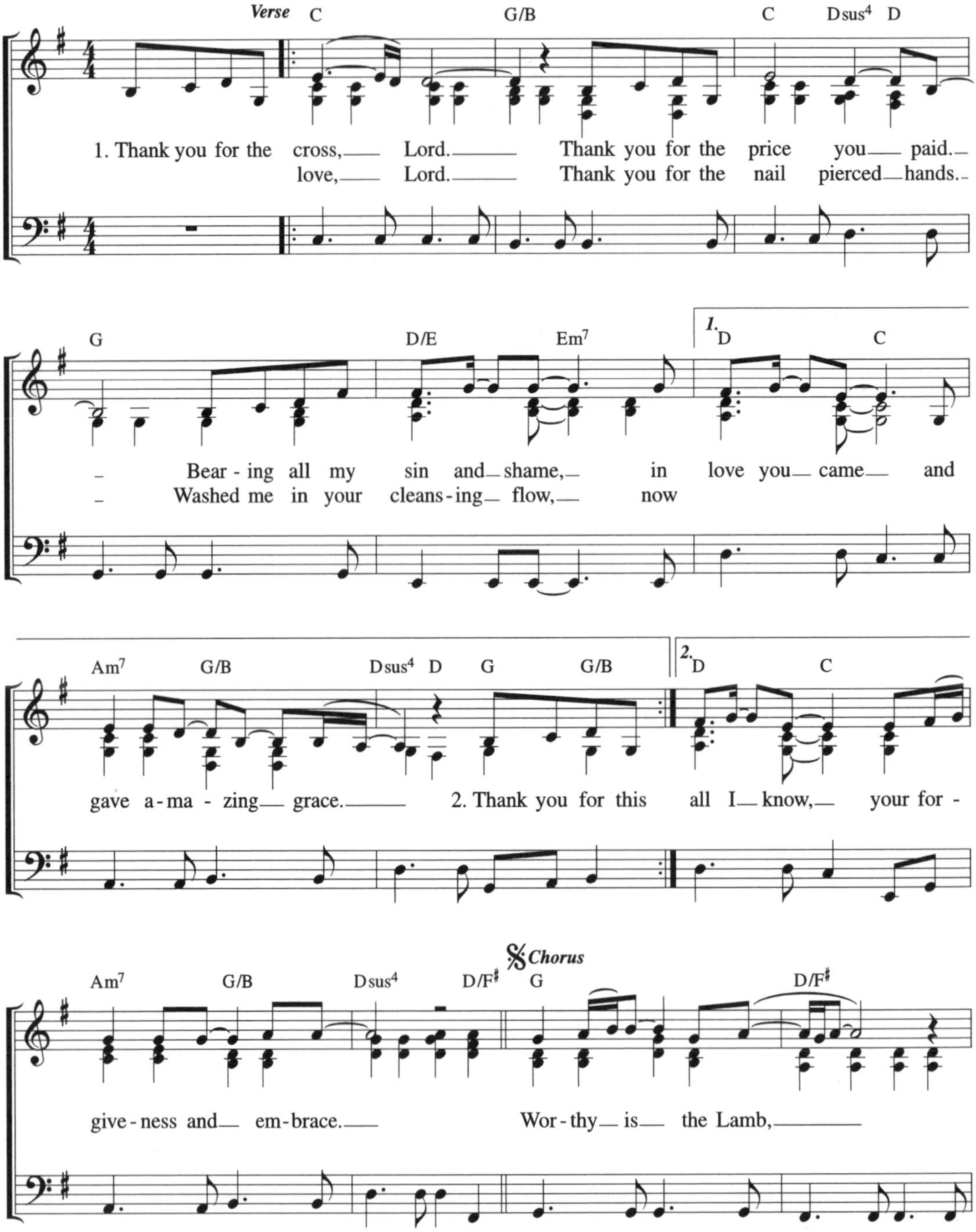
Verse
C G/B C Dsus4 D
1. Thank you for the cross, Lord. Thank you for the price you paid.
love, Lord. Thank you for the nail pierced hands.
G D/E Em7 1. D C
Bear - ing all my sin and shame, in love you came and
Washed me in your cleans - ing flow, now
Am7 G/B Dsus4 D G G/B 2. D C
gave a - ma - zing grace. 2. Thank you for this all I know, your for -
Am7 G/B Dsus4 D/F♯ Chorus G D/F♯
give - ness and em - brace. Wor - thy is the Lamb,

Suggested guitar groove 'B' (see page 125)

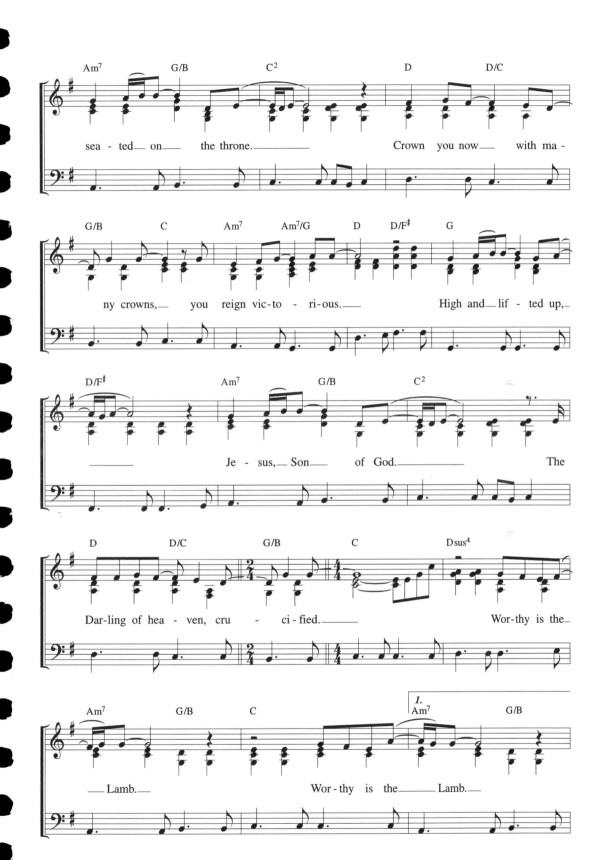

(continued over...)

106a   Collect of Easter Day

Lord of all life and power,
who through the mighty resurrection of your Son
overcame the old order of sin and death
to make all things new in him:
grant that we, being dead to sin
and alive to you in Jesus Christ,
may reign with him in glory;
to whom with you and the Holy Spirit
be praise and honour, glory and might,
now and in all eternity.

107 The King of love my Shepherd is

DOMINUS REGIT ME
Capo 2(F)

Words: Henry Williams Baker (1821-77)
Music: John Bacchus Dykes (1823-76)

Joyfully

1. The King of love my Shep-herd is, whose good-ness fail-eth ne-ver. I no-thing lack if I am his and he is mine for e-ver.

2. Where streams of liv-ing wa-ter flow my ran-somed soul he lead-eth. And where the ver-dent pa-stures grow with food ce-les-tial feed-eth.

3. Per-verse and fool-ish oft I strayed but yet in love he sought me. And on his shoul-der gen-tly laid, and home re-joi-cing brought me.

4. In death's dark vale I fear no ill, with thee dear Lord be-side me. Thy rod and staff my com-fort still, thy cross be-fore to guide me.

5. Thou spread'st a ta-ble in my sight thy unc-tion grace be-sto-weth. And O what tran-sport of de-light from thy pure cha-lice flow-eth.

6. And so through all the length of days thy good-ness fail-eth ne-ver. Good Shep-herd, may I sing thy praise with-in thy house for e-ver.

108

The Lord is gracious
and compassionate

Graham Ord

Steady 4

Suggested guitar groove 'B' or 'G' (see page 125)

109 There is a higher throne

Kristyn Lennox
& Keith Getty

1. There is a high-er throne than all this world has known, where faith-ful ones from e-very tongue will one day come. Be-fore the Son we'll stand, made fault-less through the Lamb; be-liev-ing hearts find pro-mised grace, sal-va-tion comes.

2. And there we'll find our home, our life be-fore the throne; we'll ho-nour him in per-fect song, where we be-long. He'll wipe each tear-stained eye, as thirst and hun-ger die; the Lamb be-comes our Shep-herd King, we'll reign with him.

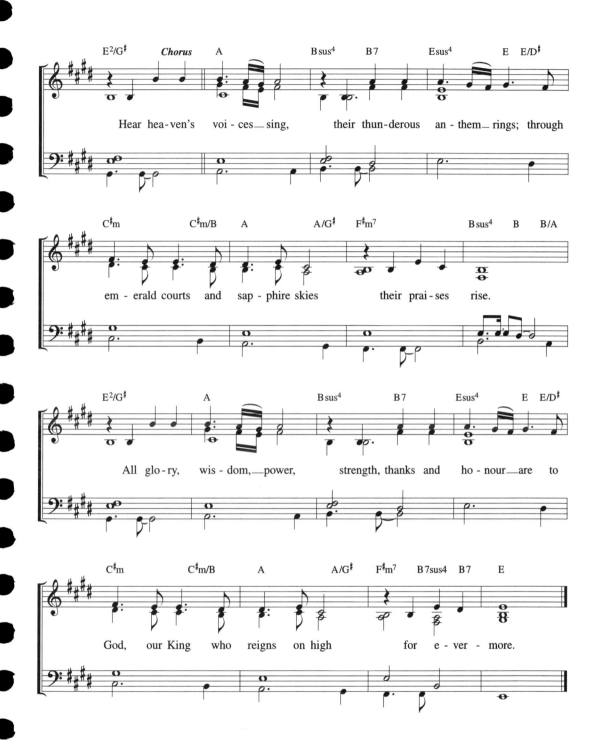

Hear hea-ven's voi-ces sing, their thun-derous an-them rings; through

em - erald courts and sap - phire skies their prai - ses rise.

All glo - ry, wis - dom, power, strength, thanks and ho - nour are to

God, our King who reigns on high for e - ver - more.

110

There is a hope so sure

Graham Kendrick

Slowly ♩ = 70

Verse

1. There is a hope so sure, a pro-mise so se-cure: the my-ste-ry of God at last made known. Trea-sures so vast ap-pear, all wis-dom, know-ledge here: it's Christ in us, the hope of glo - ry!

life so true, a life of love so pure, for all our sin a per-fect sa - cri - fice. And when that life was nailed, on cru - el cross im-paled, our sin-ful flesh with him was cru-ci - fied.

Chorus

And the life that I now live, no lon-ger

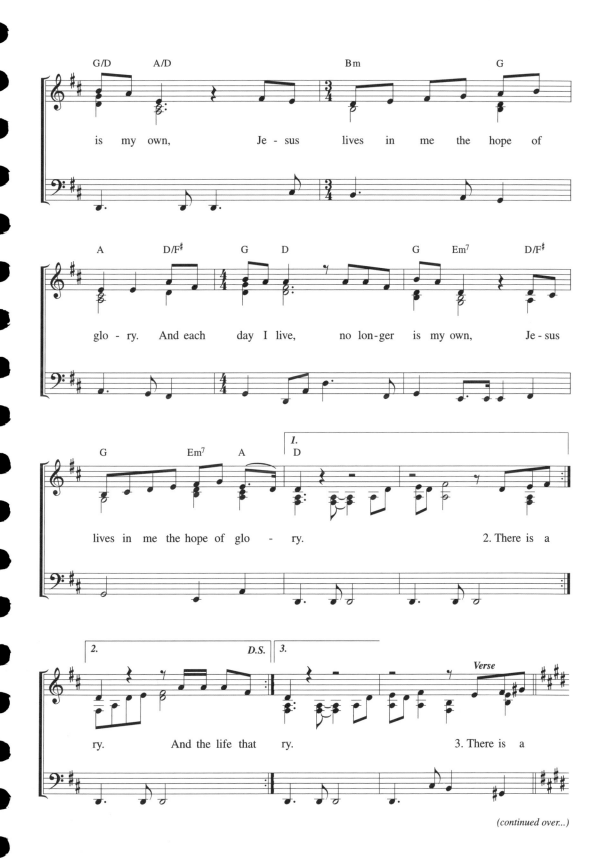

(continued over...)

life so strong, that a whole world of wrong, and all the

pow'rs of hell could not de - feat. For Je - sus

rose a-gain, and if we died with him, with him we'll rise to share his end-less

life. *Chorus* And the life that I now live, no lon-ger is my own, Je-sus

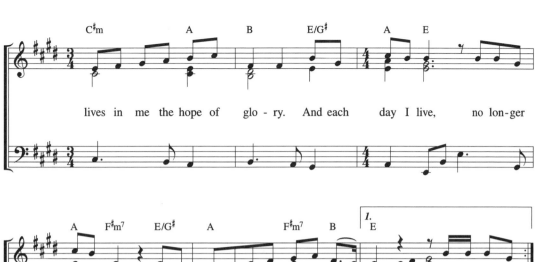

lives in me the hope of glo - ry. And each day I live, no lon-ger

is my own, Je-sus lives in me the hope of glo - ry. And the life that

To end

ry.

110a Rejoicing in the hope of the glory of God

Romans 5: 1–5

Therefore, since we have been justified through faith, we have peace with God through our Lord Jesus Christ, through whom we have gained access by faith into this grace in which we now stand. And we rejoice in the hope of the glory of God. Not only so, but we also rejoice in our sufferings, because we know that suffering produces perseverance; perseverance, character; and character, hope. And hope does not disappoint us, because God has poured out his love into our hearts by the Holy Spirit, whom he has given us.

111 There is a Redeemer

Capo 2(D)

Melody Green

1. There is a Re-deem-er, Je-sus, God's own Son, pre-cious Lamb of God, Mes-si-ah, Ho - ly One.
2. Je-sus my Re-dee-mer, name a-bove all names, pre-cious Lamb of God, Mes-si-ah, O for sin-ners slain.
3. When I stand in glo-ry I will see his face, there I'll serve my King for-e-ver in that ho-ly place.

Chorus

Thank you, O my Fa - ther, for gi-ving us your Son, and leav - ing your Spi-rit till the work on earth is done.

This song is recorded on the **Spring Harvest 20 Years Double Album**

112

Thine be the glory

MACCABEUS
Capo 2(C)
Triumphant

Words: Edmond Louis Burdy (1854-1932)
Tr. Richard Birch Hoyle (1875-1939)
Music: G.F. Handel (1685-1759)

1. Thine be the glory, risen, conquering Son;
   endless is the victory thou o'er death hast won.
   Angels in bright raiment rolled the stone away,
   kept the folded grave-clothes where thy body lay.

2. Lo, Jesus meets us, risen from the tomb!
   Lovingly he greets us, scatters fear and gloom.
   Let the church with gladness hymns of triumph sing,
   for her Lord now liveth, death hath lost its sting.

3. No more we doubt thee, glorious Prince of life;
   life is naught without thee: aid us in our strife;
   make us more than conquerors, through thy deathless love;
   lead us in thy triumph to thy home above.

113 To you, King Jesus

Nathan Fellingham

Strongly, with a half time feel

1. To you, King Jesus, we sing our song,
2. To you, King Jesus, we give our hearts,

the first and the last, the living one.
for you have come to us with your great love.

With eyes like fire, and feet like bronze, your face shines brigh-
You suf-fered death, went to the grave, but now you're crowned

ter than the sun, all cre-a-tion speaks your name.
with glory. All your peo-ple speak your name.

Suggested guitar groove 'C' (see page 125)

(continued over...)

241

114
We are a shining light
(Do something beautiful)

Graham Kendrick

1. We are a shin-ing light, ci-ty on a hill that can't be hid-den,
2. We are the salt of the earth, here to pu-ri-fy and fla-vour,

a shin-ing light. And this shin-ing light
salt of the earth. Sent through all the earth

is the life of Je-sus in us, oh what a light! The fire of his
to love God and love our neigh-bour, salt of the earth. As free-ly as

Spi-rit burns with jus-tice, joy and peace
we re-ceived so free-ly we must give,

(continued over...)

and works through our hands and feet.
and we are his hands and feet.

Chorus

Go do some-thing beau - ti - ful,___ in the name of Je - sus___

do some-thing beau - ti - ful.___ Go do some-thing Je - sus would,___

1.
___ do some-thing beau-ti - ful,___ do some-thing

beau-ti-ful.___ *2.* ___ do some-thing beau-ti-ful.___

245

115

We bow down

Gently, with awe

Viola Grafstrom

We bow down and con-fess you are Lord in this place. We bow down and con-fess you are Lord in this place. You are all I need; it's your face I seek. In the pre-sence of your light we bow down, we bow down.

Suggested guitar groove 'A' (see page 125)

116

We come in your name
(You have been lifted)

Kate Simmonds
& Mark Edwards

With energy

We come —— in your name, —— for all things —— you have made, —
— that was slain —— for our sins —— lives to reign, —

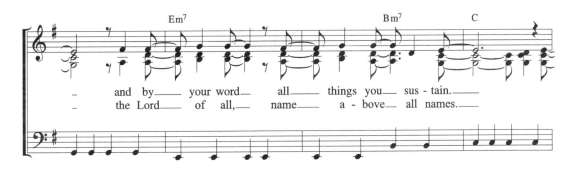

— and by —— your word —— all —— things you —— sus - tain. ——
— the Lord —— of all, —— name a - bove —— all names. ——

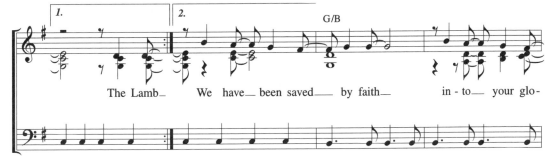

1. *2.*

The Lamb —— We have —— been saved —— by faith —— in - to —— your glo-

rious name, —— and this —— a gift —— of God, —— free - ly gi - ven us. ——

(continued over...)

Now all our sins are gone, defeated at the cross, and we now live in you, raised with you by the power of God.

Chorus

You have been lifted to the highest place, and you now live and rule forever.

We come to bring to you the highest praise, for you are King of kings

117 We could watch you from afar
(Rejoice with trembling)

Ps 2:11; Lev 9:24

Matt Redman

1. We could watch you from a-far, and for-e-ver be a-mazed at how glo-ri-ous you are. Yet, you've drawn us close to you, where the won-der's great-er still, and you o-

2. Who could ful-ly voice the praise of the God of end-less days, tell a frac-tion of your worth? For we on-ly see in part of the grace of who you are; just an e-

118   We fall down

Intensely

Chris Tomlin

Suggested guitar groove 'A' (see page 125)

Contemporary or indigenous worship?

What is 'contemporary worship'? This is not easy to describe and the definition can be subjective. When does something cease to become contemporary? Does it mean only using songs composed in the last two years? Does it mean not using historic worship practices?

A term that is starting to replace 'contemporary worship' is indigenous worship. This is worship that grows and evolves out of a particular local church's values, drawing upon the gifts and ministries of people within that worshipping community. Within our emerging culture the day of 'one size fits all' or 'one way of doing worship' is over. It is important that our worship is Jesus focussed and has biblical integrity, but within that there is not necessarily a right and wrong way to worship.

We can no longer assume that what is 'true' for, for example, a large church or a national Christian event is applicable to everywhere else. We cannot say that if it doesn't work at Spring Harvest then it is invalid. Many churches have effectively used national events as the model for their local worship; but there may come a time when a borrowed model can lose its cutting edge, when the pattern of worship no longer helps worshippers in the local congregation engage with God in the same way as before.

What implications does this have?

It may mean some songs or worship journeys used at Spring Harvest may be inappropriate for your own local church. On the other hand, some songs will fit your church like a glove. Indigenous worship grows out of the gifting of those present. So be careful in your choice of songs from the songbook. Do not assume 'one style suits all'. Choose or compose songs that are right for your own community and be at peace!

A song that is guitar-driven may not necessarily be effectively transferred to a keyboard-driven music group. Maybe the spirituality reflected in a song is not where your own congregation is at. Do not be worried if you cannot use the more complex songs in the book – there are plenty of other songs!

Indigenous worship encourages variation in worship vocabulary and practice. It doesn't matter if you have a different repertoire or worship pattern than the church up the road or this year's Spring Harvest! Some churches will exclusively use contemporary music, others a mixture of styles and worship streams, others will be into multi-sensory worship.

If you want to move into indigenous worship then try to design worship in a team, rather than leaving it to an individual, so that you reflect your community more intentionally.

David Peacock, Head of Music & Worship Department, London Bible College

119 We rejoice to be God's chosen

NETTLETON

Celtic feel

Words: John L. Bell
Tune: American trad.
Arr. David Peacock

1. We re - joice to be God's cho - sen, not through vir - tue, work or skill, but be - cause God's love is gen - erous, un-con - formed to hu - man will. And be - cause God's love is rest - less like the__ surg - ing of the

joice to be God's cho - sen, to be ga - thered to God's side, not to build a pi - ous ghet - to or be steeped in self - ish pride; but to__ ce - le - brate the good - ness of the__ one who sets us

joice to be God's cho - sen, to a - lign with heaven's in - tent, to a - wait where we are sum - moned and ac - cept where we are sent. We re - joice to be God's cho - sen and, a - midst all that we

sea,   we are pulled   by   heaven's dy - na - mic to be - come, not just to
free   from the small - ness   of   our   vi - sion to be - come, not just to
see,   to an - ti - ci - pate with won - der that the best   is   yet to

1.,2.   **3.**

be.   2. We re -
be.   3. We re -
be.

119a   Living as God's chosen people
Colossians 3: 12–14

Therefore, as God's chosen people, holy and dearly loved, clothe yourselves with compassion, kindness, humility, gentleness and patience. Bear with each other and forgive whatever grievances you may have against one another. Forgive as the Lord forgave you. And over all these virtues put on love, which binds them all together in perfect unity.

120 We will proclaim

Geraldine Latty

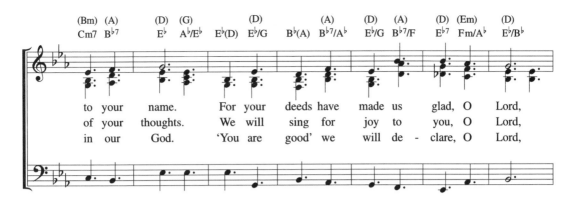

to your name. For your deeds have made us glad, O Lord,
of your thoughts. We will sing for joy to you, O Lord,
in our God. 'You are good' we will de - clare, O Lord,

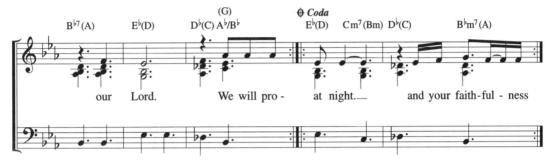

our Lord.   We will pro -   at night.___   and your faith-ful - ness

at night.___

120a A Prayer of Dedication

Almighty God,
we thank you for the gift of your holy word.
May it be a lantern to our feet,
a light to our paths,
and a strength to our lives.
Take us and use us
to love and serve
in the power of the Holy Spirit
and in the name of your Son,
Jesus Christ our Lord.
Amen.

121

We've come to sing
(Everybody sing)

Dave Bilbrough

With a slight driving feel

We've come to sing our songs of worship; we've come to give ourselves in praise, to offer thanks to our creator, and celebrate the one who saves. one who saves. Everybody sing of his everlasting love. Everybody sing of his everlasting love. He's slow to anger,

rich in mer - cy; let all the earth— de-clare— his glo - ry. E-very - bo-dy sing of his e-

ver - last - ing love.—

E-very-bo- Al - le - lu - ia!

E - ver-last - ing love.—

122 What a friend we have in Jesus

CONVERSE
Capo 3(D)
Peacefully

Words: Joseph Medlicot Scriven (1819-86)
Music: Charles Crozat Converse (1832-1918)

1. What a friend we have in Je - sus, all our sins and griefs to bear!
What a pri-vi-lege to car - ry e - very-thing to God in prayer!
O what peace we of - ten for - feit! O what need-less pain we bear!
All be-cause we do not car - ry e - very-thing to God in prayer.

2. Have we trials and temptations?
Is there trouble anywhere?
We should never be discouraged;
take it to the Lord in prayer.
Can we find a friend so faithful
who will all our sorrows share?
Jesus knows our every weakness;
take it to the Lord in prayer.

3. Are we weak and heavy-laden,
cumbered with a load of care?
Precious Saviour, still our refuge,
take it to the Lord in prayer.
Do thy friends despise, forsake thee?
Take it to the Lord in prayer;
in his arms he'll take and shield thee,
thou wilt find a solace there.

Bridges to F

261

123

What does the Lord require of me?

With an 'island' feel

Dave Bilbrough

What does the Lord re - quire of me; what does he ask— me from my

heart? What does the Lord re - quire of me; but to

Last time to Coda

act just-ly, and to love mer-cy, and walk hum - bly with the

Lord my God. Take all— my life till there's no-thing— be-tween my

Suggested guitar groove 'G' (see page 125)

124

What love is this?

Doug Horley
& Steve Whitehouse

Simply

Verse

1. What love is this?_____ The love of Je - sus,____ that gave its
   King,____ you are my Sa - viour,____ you'll al - ways
   pow'r____ rain down up - on me;____ such peace and

all,_____ that cost his life.____ Flesh torn by nails,____ life cruel - ly
be_____ a friend to me.____ Safe in your arms____ now and for -
joy____ cas - ca - ding down.____ May your love touch____ all those a -

ta - ken,_____ the Fa - ther's Son,_____ love's sa - cri -
e - ver;_____ your love shines bright,_____ my morn - ing
round me;_____ I'll shine for you,_____ I'll shine for

Chorus

fice.____ And I thank you, Lord,____ for lov - ing me,____ and I lift my
star.____
you.____

hands_____ so grate - ful - ly._____ And I thank you, Lord,_____ that I can

be_____ a child of yours_____ e - ter - nal - ly.

2. You are my
3. Now let your

124a   Lord, have mercy (Kyrie)

Salvation comes from the Lord,
the God of heaven who made the sea and the land.
whose mercy extends to all people.

Lord, have mercy.
Lord, have mercy.

Salvation comes from the Lord,
who longs to see all people turning from their evil ways
that he might show them mercy and have compassion.

Christ, have mercy.
Christ, have mercy.

Salvation comes from the Lord,
who is gracious, slow to anger and abounding in love.
In mercy, he relents from sending calamity.

Lord, have mercy.
Lord, have mercy.

125 What wonder of grace is this
(My desire)

Stuart Townend

Not too fast

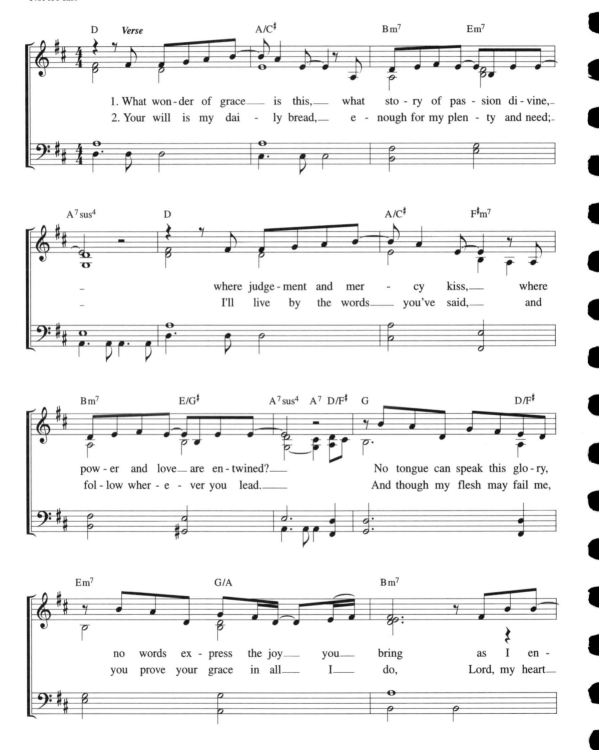

1. What won-der of grace is this, what sto-ry of pas-sion di-vine,
2. Your will is my dai-ly bread, e-nough for my plen-ty and need;

where judge-ment and mer-cy kiss, where
I'll live by the words you've said, and

pow-er and love are en-twined? No tongue can speak this glo-ry,
fol-low wher-e-ver you lead. And though my flesh may fail me,

no words ex-press the joy you bring as I en-
you prove your grace in all I do, Lord, my heart

126

When I turn my eyes
(Lift my eyes)

Moderately

Steve James

(continued over...)

heat of— the day. No e - vil— pre - vails in his pur - pose— for me, till his

face I see.——— Lift my

126a   Call to worship

Let us worship together the Lord, the God of heaven, who made the sea and the land.

Let us urgently call on his name that he might show us his salvation.

Let us seek his forgiveness and know his healing love that we might be empowered in the service of righteousness and truth.

Copyright © 2003 Marie Birkinshaw

127

When I survey

ROCKINGHAM

Peacefully

Words: Isaac Watts (1674-1748)
Music: 18th Century melody
Adpt. Edward Miller (1731-1807)

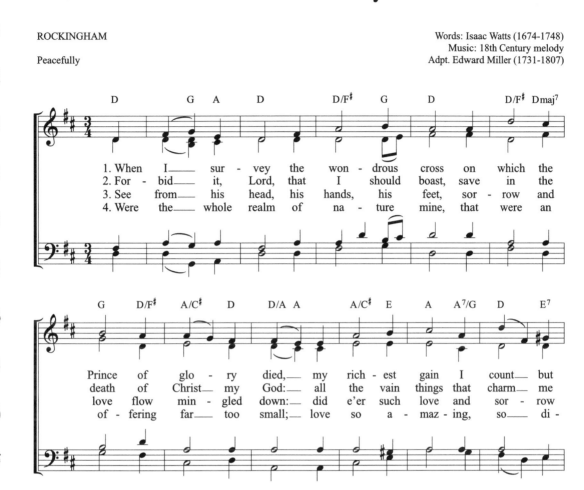

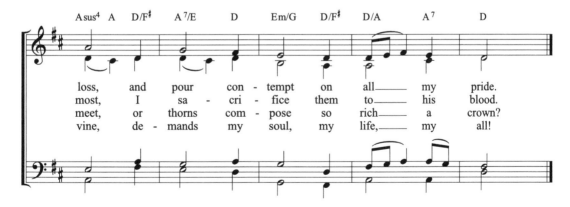

1. When I sur - vey the won - drous cross on which the Prince of glo - ry died, my rich - est gain I count but loss, and pour con - tempt on all my pride.

2. For - bid it, Lord, that I should boast, save in the death of Christ my God: all the vain things that charm me most, I sa - cri - fice them to his blood.

3. See from his head, his hands, his feet, sor - row and love flow min - gled down: did e'er such love and sor - row meet, or thorns com - pose so rich a crown?

4. Were the whole realm of na - ture mine, that were an of - fering far too small; love so a - maz - ing, so di - vine, de - mands my soul, my life, my all!

Suggested guitar groove 'H' (see page 125)
This song is recorded on the double album Celebrating 25 Years of Spring Harvest

271

128

When I was lost
(There is a new song)

Capo 3 (D)

Gospel feel

Kate & Miles Simmonds

Verse

1. When I was lost, you came and res-cued me;___
   You know all the things I've e-ver done,___
2. Now I have come in-to your fa-mi-ly,___
   In the full as-su-rance of your love___

reached down in-to the pit and lif-ted me.___ O Lord,
but Je-sus' blood has can-celled e-v'ry one.___ O Lord,
for the Son of God has died for me.___ O Lord,
now with ev-'ry con-fi-dence we come.___ O Lord,

1.,3.
such love,___ I was as far from you___ as I could be.___
such grace___ to qua-li-
such peace,___ I am as loved by you___ as I could be.___
such joy___ to know that

2.,4.
fy me as___ your own.___
you de-light___ in me.

Chorus
There is a new song
stand firm

This song is recorded on the Spring Harvest 2002 New Songs Album & the 2002 Live Worship Album

(continued over...)

and ma-ny are___ the things___ that you___ have planned.___

How beau-ti-ful___ the grace___ that gives___ to us___ all that we don't___

___ de-serve,___ all that we can - not earn,___ but is a gift___ of love.___

Your love has lif-ted me.

D.S. al Coda ⊕ *Coda*

There is a me.

129

When peace like a river
(It is well)

Philip Bliss
& Horatio Spafford

Gospel feel

(optional melody)

(3.) sin,   oh   the   bliss   of   this

Verse

1. When   peace   like   a   ri - ver   at -
(2.)   Sa - tan   should   buf - fet,   though
(4.)   Lord,   haste   the   day   when   my

glo - ri - ous   thought,   my   sin,   not   in

ten - deth   my   way,   when   sor - rows   like
tri - als   should   come,   let   bles - sed   as -
faith   shall   be   sight,   the   clouds   be   rolled

part,   but   in   whole   is   nailed   to   the

sea - bil - lows   roll,   what - e - ver   my
sur - rance   con - trol   that   Christ   hath   re -
back   as   a   scroll;   the   trump   shall   re -

(continued over...)

cross____ and I____ bear   it   no   more;____   praise___the Lord,

F   D/F#   G

lot,____   thou hast taught   me to   say:____   it   is
gar - ded   my   help - less e - state____   and hath
sound   and   the   Lord   shall de - scend;____   e - ven

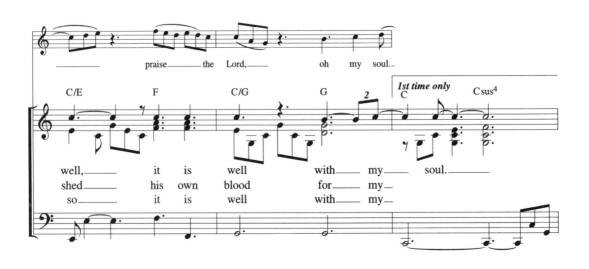

____ praise____the Lord,____   oh   my   soul._

C/E   F   C/G   G   *1st time only*
                                                               C   Csus⁴

well,____   it   is   well   with____ my____ soul.____
shed____   his own blood   for____ my_
so____   it   is   well   with____ my_

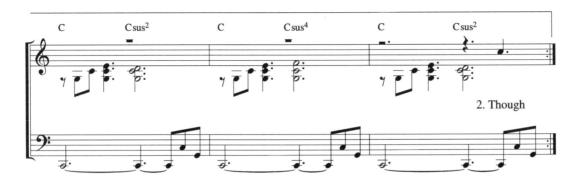

C   Csus²   C   Csus⁴   C   Csus²

2. Though

130   When love came down

Stuart Townend

Tenderly

1. When love came down to earth and made his home with men, the hope-less found a hope, the sin-ner found a friend. Not to the pow-er-ful but to the poor he came, and hum-ble, hun-gry hearts were sa-tis-fied a-gain.

2. thought, and ev-'ry sin-ful deed was scourged up-on his back and ham-mered through his feet; The in-no-cent is cursed, the guil-ty are re-leased; the pu-nish-ment of God on God has brought me peace.— What

3. load down at the Ma-ster's feet; your shame will be re-moved, your joy will be com-plete. Come cru-ci-fy your pride, and en-ter as a child; for those who bow down low he'll lift up to his side.

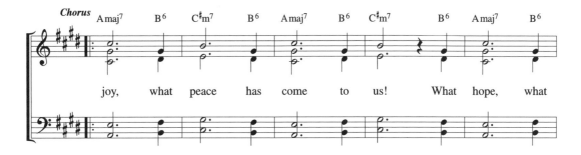

joy,   what   peace   has   come   to   us!   What   hope,   what

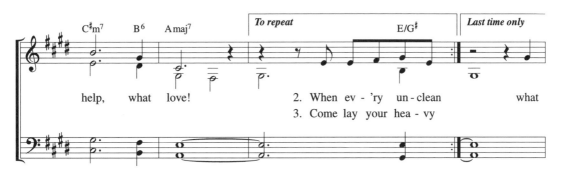

help,   what   love!

2. When ev - 'ry un - clean   what
3. Come lay your hea - vy

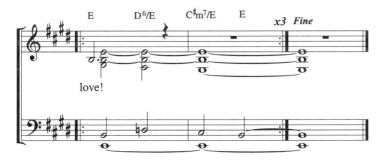

love!

130a Prayer of Mission

Eternal God, giver of love and power,
your Son Jesus Christ has sent us into all the world
to preach the gospel of his kingdom:
confirm us in this mission,
and help us to live the good news we proclaim;
through Jesus Christ our Lord.

131
When the music fades
(The heart of worship)

Capo 1(D)

Matt Redman

Steadily

1. When the mu - sic fades,___ all is stripped a - way,___
2. King of end - less worth,___ no one could ex - press___

___ and I sim - ply come; long - ing just to bring___
___ how much you de - serve.___ Though I'm weak and poor,___

___ some - thing that's of worth___ that will bless your heart.___
___ all I have is yours,___ ev - ery sin - gle breath.___

I'll bring you more than a song,___ for a song in it - self

is not what you have re - quired.___ You search much deep - er with - in___

Suggested guitar groove 'B' or 'C' (see page 125)
This song is recorded on the Spring Harvest Ultimate Praise Mix Double Album

through the way things ap - pear; you're look - ing in - to my heart.

I'm com - ing back to the heart of wor - ship, and it's

all a - bout you, all a - bout you, Je - sus. I'm sor - ry, Lord, for the thing

I've made it, when it's all a - bout you, all a - bout you, Je - sus.

132 Who compares to you?
(Magnificent)

Raymond Badham

132a Incomparable

Exodus 15: 11

'Who among the gods is like you, O Lord?
    Who is like you – majestic in glory, working wonders?'

133
With a prayer
(Love incarnate)

Stuart Townend

1. With a

Verse

pray'r you fed the hun - gry, with a cry you stilled the storm; with a look you had com - pas - sion on the de - sp'rate and for - lorn. With a touch you healed the le - per, with a shout you raised the

sheep be - fore the shea - rer you were si - lent in your pain; you en - dured hu - mi - li - a - tion at the hands of those you'd made. And as hell un - leashed its fu - ry you were lif - ted on a

feed the poor and hun - gry, I will stand up for the truth; I will take my cross and fol - low to the cor - ners of the earth. And I ask that you so fill me with your peace, your pow'r, your

This song is recorded on the Spring Harvest 2003 New Songs Album

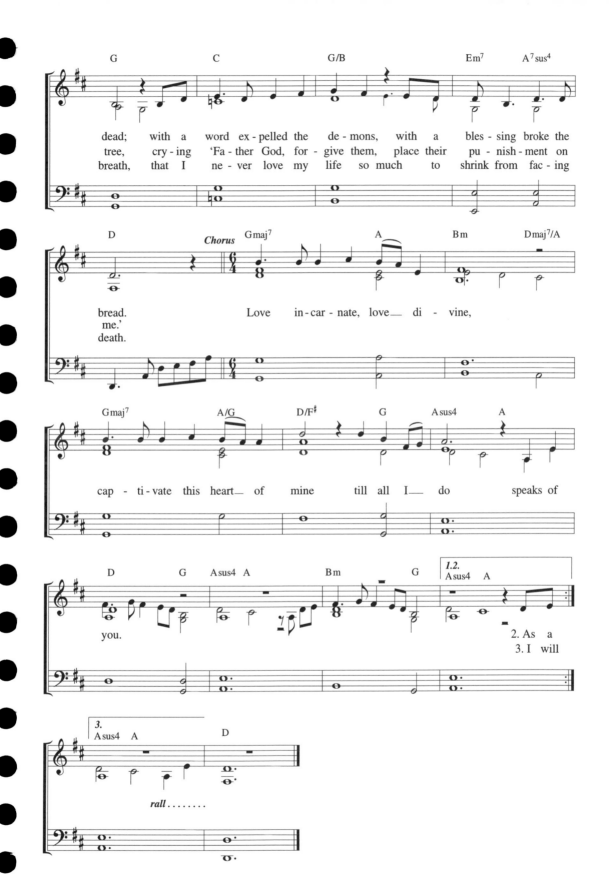

dead; with a word ex-pelled the de-mons, with a bles-sing broke the
tree, cry-ing 'Fa-ther God, for-give them, place their pu-nish-ment on
breath, that I ne-ver love my life so much to shrink from fac-ing

bread.
me.'
death.

Love in-car-nate, love— di - vine,

cap - ti-vate this heart— of mine till all I— do speaks of

you.

2. As a
3. I will

rall . . . .

134 With a true heart
(Be my all)

Steve McGregor

1. With a true heart, Lord, we en - ter in -
2. In all we do, all our ways ac - know -
3. Chan - ges in time, winds that blow may cause

to your pre - sence. Bright Morn - ing Star,
ledge your pur - pose. We reach for you,
some di - strac - tion. We keep our minds

draw - ing near, in awe of your great - ness. Be my all in
need you, Lord, to guide and di - rect us.
stayed on you, whose love is un - fail - ing.

all, ev-'ry beat my heart de-si-res just to know you

more: this time, this place we come to wor - ship

to wor - ship you.

134a Coming into God's presence

Almighty God,
your Son has opened for us
a new and living way into your presence.
Give us new hearts and constant wills
to worship you in spirit and in truth;
through Jesus Christ our Lord.
Amen.

From Methodist Worship Book (Methodist Publishing House, 1999) Copyright © Trustees for Methodist Church Purposes 1999.

135 Wonderful, so wonderful
(Beautiful One)

Tim Hughes

1. Won-der-ful, so won-der-ful is your un-fail-ing love, your
2. Po-wer-ful, so po-wer-ful, your glo-ry fills the skies, your

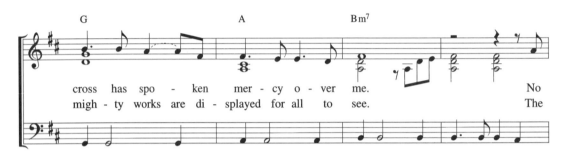

cross has spo-ken mer-cy o-ver me. No
might-y works are di-splayed for all to see. The

eye has seen, no ear has heard, no heart could ful-ly know how
beau-ty of your ma-je-sty a-wakes my heart to sing: how

glo-ri-ous, how beau-ti-ful you are. Beau-ti-ful one I
mar-vel-lous, how won-der-ful you are.

Suggested guitar groove 'E' (see page 125)
This song is recorded on the Spring Harvest 2003 New Songs Album

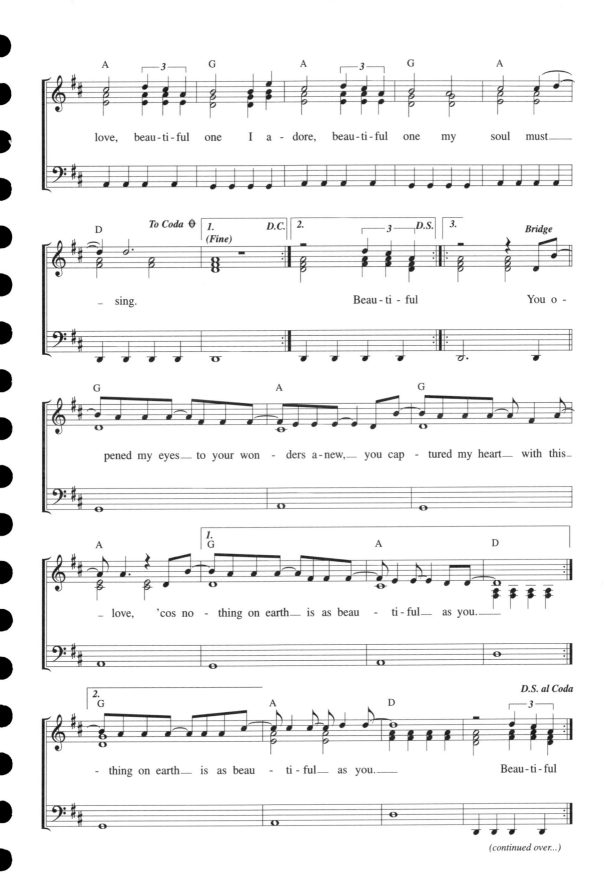

$\oplus$ *Coda*

My soul,— my soul— must sing.— My soul,—

— my soul— must sing.— My soul,— my soul— must sing.—

Beau-ti-ful one.— Beau-ti-ful

135a   God's revelation to us by his Holy Spirit

1 Corinthians 2: 9 & 10

However as it is written:

> 'No eye has seen,
> 　　no ear has heard,
> no mind has conceived
> 　　what God has prepared for
> 　　those who love him'

but God has revealed it to us by his Spirit.
The Spirit searches all things, even the deep things of God.

Tips for Sound Engineers

Know your system – Think of your system as an 'audio chain' made up of five components: input, control, amplifiers, speakers and cabling. Look at each area; try to understand what it's doing and how you can get the best out of it. Thinking this way will also help you when you're fault finding.

Setting up – The time before the band turns up is precious. Have as much, if not all of the equipment, mics and DIs set up and checked before musicians get on stage. Have two or three cable routes on stage and stick to them. Being tidy will pay off if there is a problem and a cable needs to be changed.

Start levels – Before the band start 'making a noise' set a starting level in the main PA and foldback on all vocal mics. Find the maximum level before feedback occurs in the PA and foldback; and make a note of these settings. Do not go above these settings during the meeting.

Monitor Mixes – Monitors enable a musician or singer to hear themselves and one or two other key instruments so they keep in tune and time. The sound produced by the foldback can be counter productive to the balance and levels through the front-of-house PA. Keeping monitors simple is the key. Only give the musicians and vocalists the minimum amount of level they need to work with.

Microphone technique – The closer a mic is to the source of sound the more audio level you will get from it. With instruments like drums and guitars there is not usually a problem with level, but with quieter sounds there can be. Invariably it's the vocals that have problems; try getting singers to sing close and down the axis of the mic or sing up in volume. The more level vocalists give you the more you can give them in their monitors before feedback occurs. The additional benefit of this is that they will also get less spill into their mics from other instruments.

Be attentive – Keep a finger on the worship leader's fader so you don't miss ad libbing. Anticipate speech mics being used at short notice as well as instrument solos. Mix with your head up and scan the stage, don't be caught out.

Simon Ward

136 Yes, I believe
(Jesus first)

Judy Bailey

Suggested guitar groove 'C' (see page 125)
This song is recorded on the Spring Harvest 2003 New Songs Album

Je - sus,— Je - sus,— in all I do, Je - sus,— Je - sus,—

help me re - mem - ber,— that first of all comes you.

136a Faith in the Son of God

1 John 5: 1–5

Everyone who believes that Jesus is the Christ is born of God, and everyone who loves the father loves his child as well. This is how we know that we love the children of God: by loving God and carrying out his commands. This is love for God: to obey his commands. And his commands are not burdensome, for everyone born of God has overcome the world. This is the victory that has overcome the world, even our faith. Who is it that overcomes the world? Only he who believes that Jesus is the Son of God.

137 You are God in heaven
(Let my words be few)

Steadily

Matt & Beth Redman

Lyrics:

You are God in hea - ven, and here am I on earth;
The sim-plest of all love songs I want to bring to you;
so I'll let my words be few: Je-
so I'll let my words be few: Je-
sus, I am so in love with you. And I'll
sus, I am so in love with you.
stand in awe of you, yes, I'll
stand in awe of you. And I'll

Suggested guitar groove 'A' or 'B' (see page 125)
This song is recorded on the Spring Harvest 2001 Live Worship Album & on the double album Celebrating 25 Years of Spring Harvest

let my words— be few:——— Je - sus, I— am so— in love— with you.—

To repeat

To end

Fine

137a Prayer after communion (2)

Father of all,
we give you thanks and praise,
that when we were still far off
you met us in your Son and brought us home.
Dying and living, he declared your love,
gave us grace, and opened the gate of glory.
May we who share Christ's body live his risen life;
we who drink his cup bring life to others;
we whom the Spirit lights give light to the world.
Keep us firm in the hope you have set before us,
so we and all your children shall be free,
and the whole earth live to praise your name;
through Christ our Lord.
Amen.

From Common Worship: Services and Prayers for the Church of England. Copyright © The Archbishops' Council 2000

138 You are my anchor

Stuart Townend

With a steady rock feel

1. You are my an - chor,— my light and my sal - va - tion.
(2.) — Lord,— make straight the path be - fore— me.

You are my re - fuge,— my heart will not fear.—
Do not for - sake— me, my hope is in you.—

Though my foes— sur - round— me on ev - 'ry hand,— they will stum-
As I walk— through life,— I am con - fi - dent— I will see—

ble and fall— while in grace— I stand.— In my day— of trou - ble, you hide—
— your good - ness— with e - ve - ry step,— and my heart— di - rects— me to seek—

me and set— me a-bove——————————— to sing this song— of love:—
you in all— that I do,——————————— so I will wait— for you.—

Chorus One thing I will ask— of you, this will I pray:— to dwell in your house,—

O Lord, e-ve-ry day;— to gaze— u-pon— your love - ly face,—

and rest—— in the Fa - ther's em-brace.——

(Fine)

D.C. al fine

2. Teach me your way,—

139 You are the healing oil

Trish Morgan

Capo 3(D)

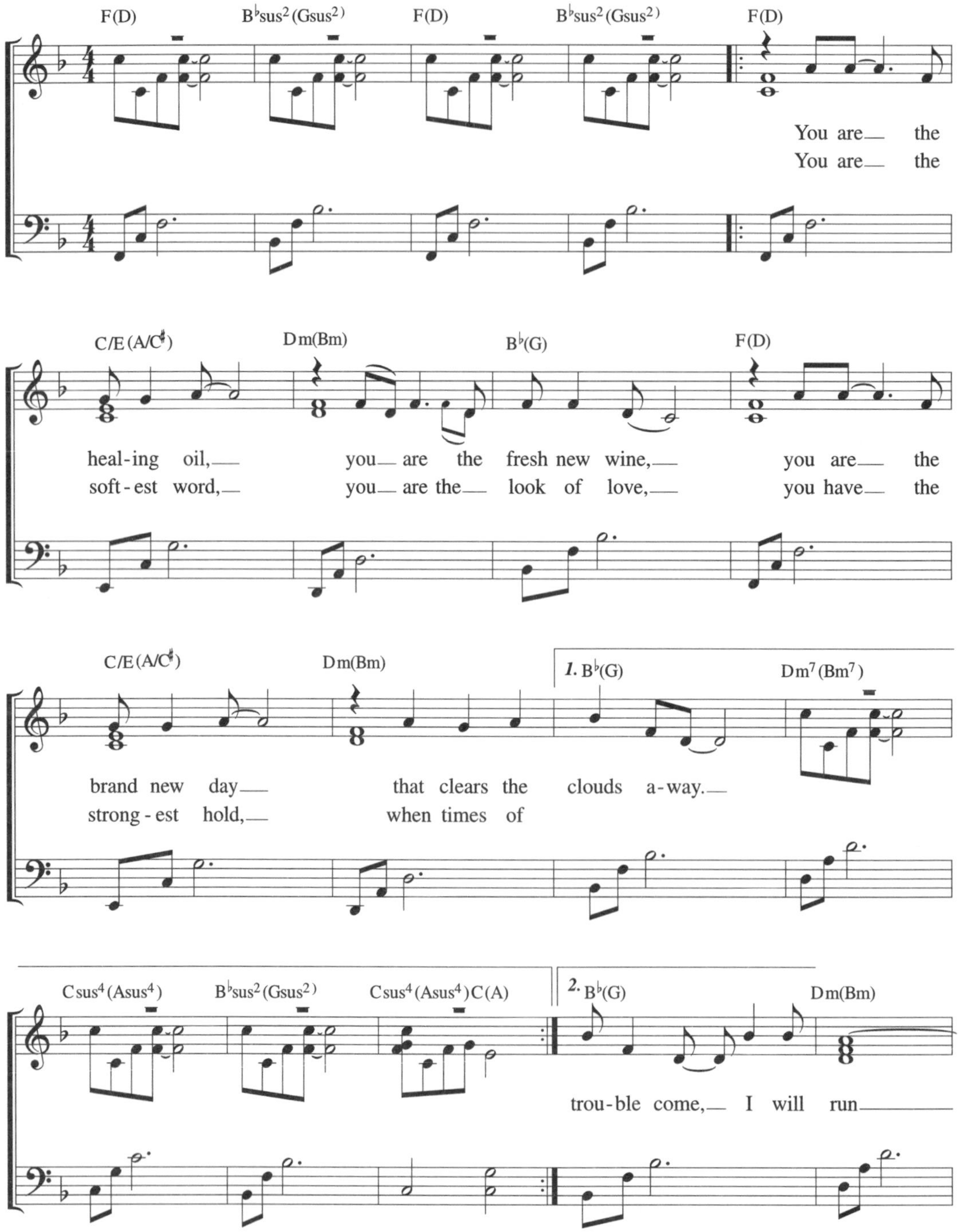
F(D) B♭sus2(Gsus2) F(D) B♭sus2(Gsus2) F(D)
You are the healing oil, you are the fresh new wine, you are the brand new day that clears the clouds away.
You are the softest word, you are the look of love, you have the strongest hold, when times of trouble come, I will run
C/E(A/C♯) Dm(Bm) B♭(G) F(D)
C/E(A/C♯) Dm(Bm) 1. B♭(G) Dm7(Bm7)
Csus4(Asus4) B♭sus2(Gsus2) Csus4(Asus4) C(A) 2. B♭(G) Dm(Bm)

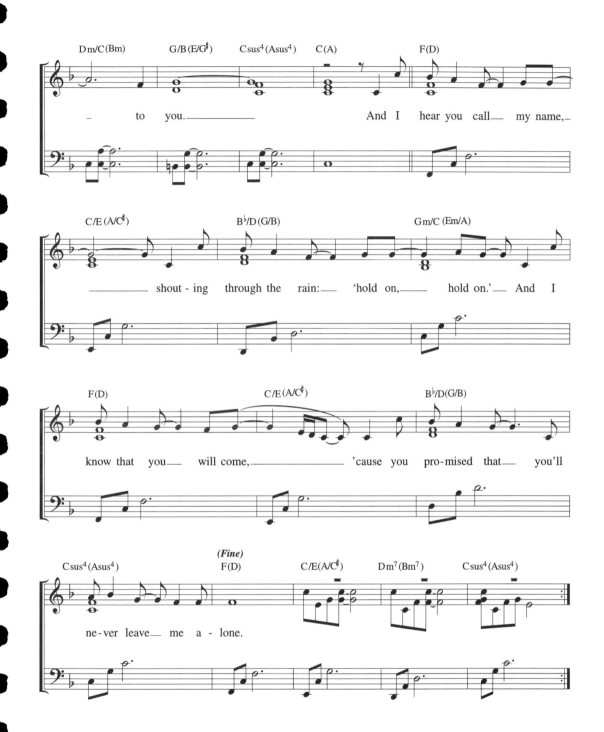

to you._____ And I hear you call___ my name,___

_____ shout - ing through the rain:___ 'hold on,_____ hold on.'___ And I

know that you___ will come,_____ 'cause you pro-mised that___ you'll

(Fine)

ne - ver leave___ me a - lone.

140 You are the Lord, the Famous One
(Famous One)

Chris Tomlin
& Jesse Reeves

With excitement

Lyrics:
You are the Lord, the fa-mous one, fa-mous one; great is your name in all the earth. The hea-vens de-clare you're glo-ri-ous, glo-ri-ous; great is your fame be-yond the earth.

(continued over...)

lone are God.
beau - ti - ful.

the earth.

140a The glory of God in creation

Psalm 19: 1–4a

The heavens declare the glory of God;
    the skies proclaim the work of his hands.
Day after day they pour forth speech;
    night after night they display knowledge.
There is no speech or language
    where their voice is not heard.
Their voice goes out into all the earth,
    their words to the ends of the world.

Bridges to G

141 You are the Lord, the King of heaven
(Glorious)

Mick Goss
& Eoghan Heaslip

♩ = 105

You are___ the Lord,___ the King of hea - ven and all___ the earth,
Be - fore___ your throne___ the el - ders fall,___ and an - gels sing:___

___ you'll reign for - e - ver. First and___ the last,___ you are
___ 'Al - migh - ty God.'___ Bright Mor - ing Star,___

glo-ri-ous,___ you are___ glo - ri-

ous, you - are___ glo - ri - ous. To

Suggested guitar groove 'A' or 'B' (see page 125)

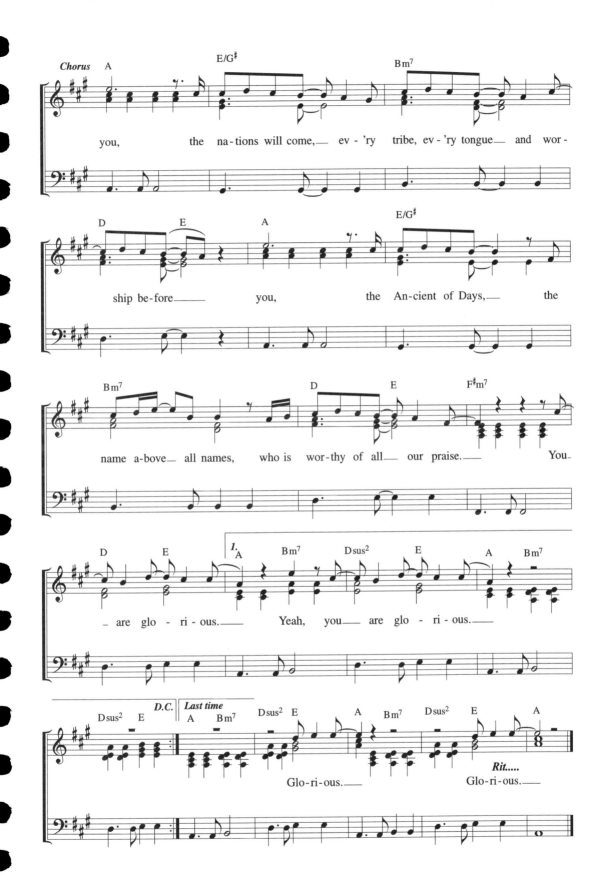

142 You chose the cross
(Lost in wonder)

Capo 3(G)

Steadily

Martyn Layzell

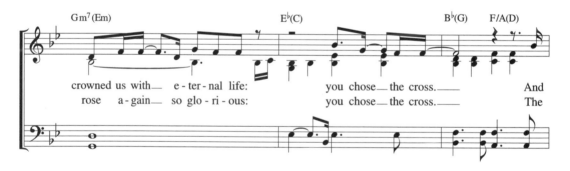

1. You chose the cross with ev'ry breath, the perfect life, the perfect death:
loosed the cords of sinfulness and broke the chains of my disgrace:

you chose the cross. A crown of thorns you wore for us, and
you chose the cross. Up from the grave victorious you

crowned us with eternal life: you chose the cross. And
rose again so glorious: you chose the cross. The

though your soul was overwhelmed with pain, o-
sorrow that surrounded you was mine, 'yet

This song is recorded on the Spring Harvest 2003 New Songs Album

143 Your hand O God
(One church)

Capo 3(G)

Steadily

Music: Keith Getty
Words: E. H. Plumtree (1821-91) adpt. Keith Getty

1. Your hand, O God, has gui-ded your church from age to age, the tale of love is writ-ten for us on ev-'ry page. Our fa-thers knew your good-ness, and we, your works re-cord, and each of these bear wit-ness: one—

mer-cy ne-ver fails us, or leaves your work un-done; with your right hand to help us, the vic-t'ry shall be won. And then with hea-ven's an-gels your name shall be a-dored, and they shall praise you, sing-ing: one—

144 You hold the sea
(All honour)

Russ Hughes

1. You hold the sea in the palm of your hand
2. You ride from hea-ven up-on a white horse,

and cause the moun-tains to trem-ble.
your eyes are blaz-ing with fire.

You call the na-tions to
Thou-sands of an-gels are

bow at your throne and bring its ru-lers to judge-ment! The
fol-low-ing on, you strike the na-tions with judge-ment! The

Lord is your name let all earth pro-claim.

All ho - nour,— all pow - er,— all glo - ry— be -

longs to— you, Lord! longs to— you, Lord! The an - gels cry 'ho - ly,' the

an - gels cry 'ho - ly is the Lord.' The

Lord.' Lord.'

145 You hear, O Lord

Graham Kendrick

Steadily ♩ = 113

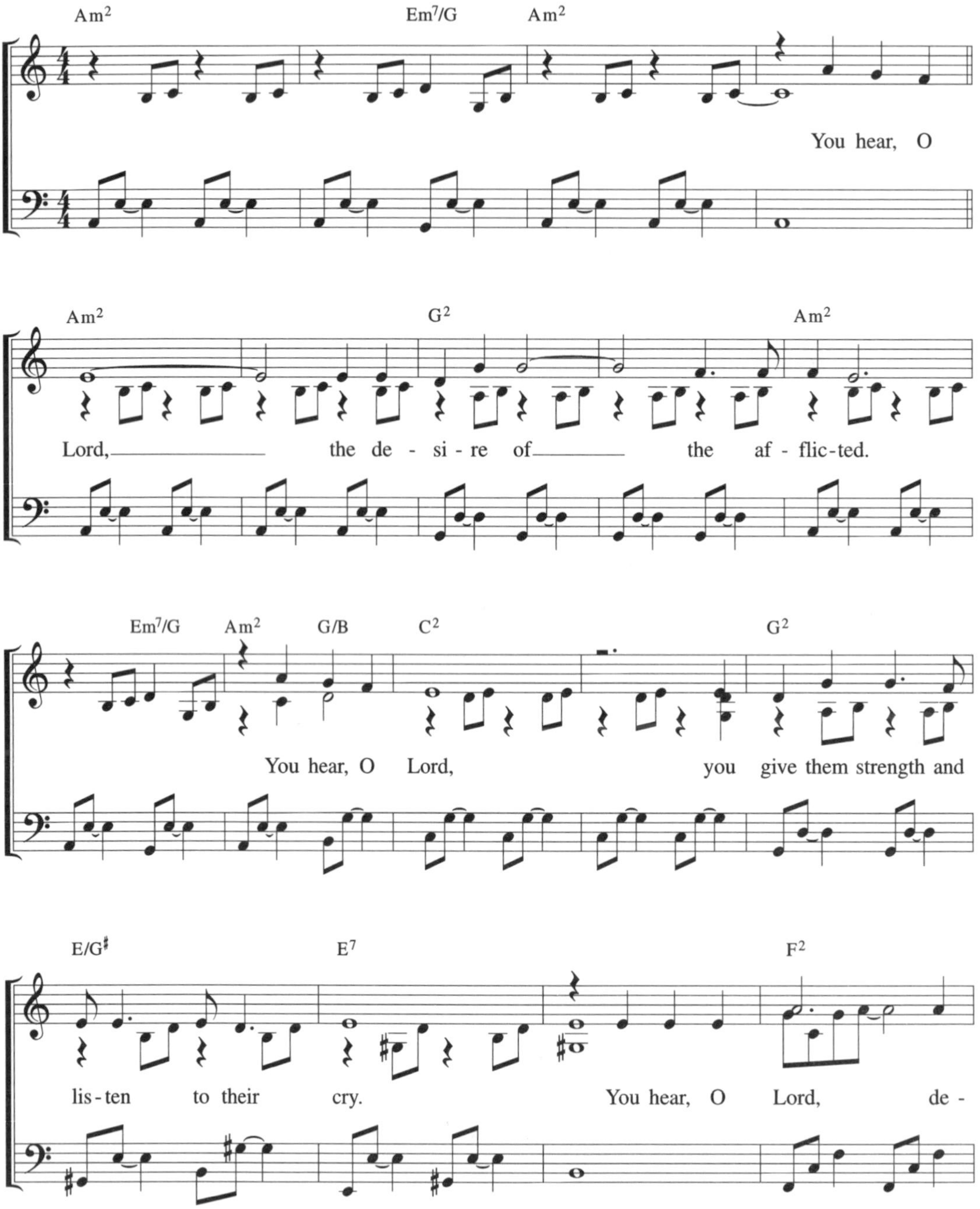

Am2 Em7/G Am2
You hear, O
Am2 G2 Am2
Lord, the de - si - re of the af - flic-ted.
Em7/G Am2 G/B C2 G2
You hear, O Lord, you give them strength and
E/G♯ E7 F2
lis-ten to their cry. You hear, O Lord, de -

This song is recorded on the Spring Harvest 2002 Live Worship Album

(continued over...)

146 Your love is amazing
(Hallelujah)

Brian Doerksen
& Brenton Brown

♩ = 96

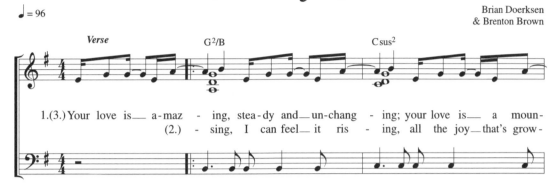

Verse

1.(3.) Your love is a-maz - ing, stea-dy and un-chang - ing; your love is a moun-
(2.) - sing, I can feel it ris - ing, all the joy that's grow-

- tain, firm be-neath my feet. Your love is a mys-
ing deep in-side of me. E - v'ry time I see

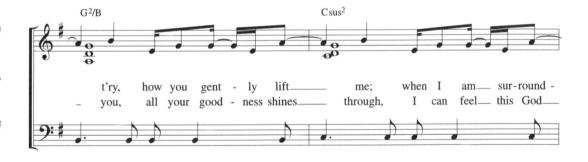

t'ry, how you gent - ly lift me; when I am sur-round -
- you, all your good - ness shines through, I can feel this God

ed, your love car - ries me. Hal-le-lu - jah, hal-le-lu-
- song ris-ing up in me.

(continued over...)

Suggested guitar groove 'D' (see page 125)
This song is recorded on the Spring Harvest 2001 New Songs Album

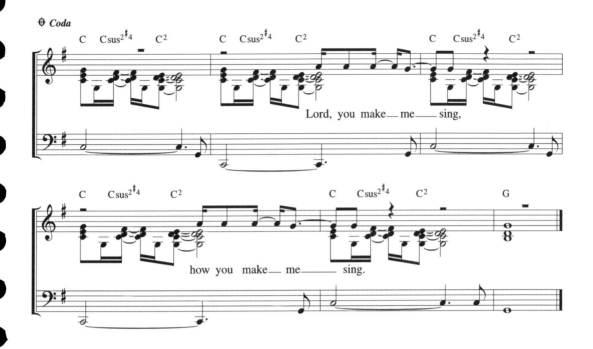

⊕ *Coda*

Lord, you make — me — sing,

how you make — me — sing.

146a Sing to the Lord!

Psalm 108: 1–5

My heart is steadfast, O God;
    I will sing and make music with all my soul.
Awake, harp and lyre!
    I will awaken the dawn.
I will praise you, O Lord,
        among the nations;
        I will sing of you among the peoples.
For great is your love, higher than the heavens;
    your faithfulness reaches to the skies.
Be exalted, O God, above the heavens,
        and let your glory be over all the earth.

147 You shine
(Why should I fear man?)

Brian Doerksen

Suggested guitar groove 'E' or 'F' (see page 125)

(continued over...)

148 You spread out the skies
(Wonderful Maker)

Matt Redman
& Chris Tomlin

Verse C   Em⁷sus⁴

1. You spread out the skies   o - ver emp - ty space,   said 'Let there be light;' to a

C   D   G/B

dark   and form - less world   your light was born.

C   Em⁷

2. You spread out your arms   o - ver emp - ty hearts,   said 'Let there be light;' to a
(3.) eye has ful - ly seen how beau - ti - ful the cross, and we have on - ly heard the⎯

C   D

dark   and hope - less world   your Son was born.
faint - est whis - pers of how great you are.   You

(continued over...)

Suggested guitar groove 'B' (see page 125)

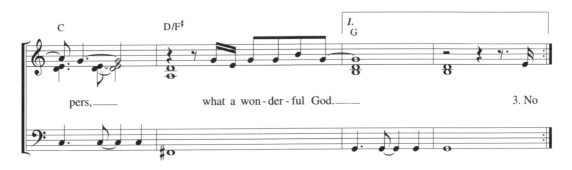

pers,——

what a won-der-ful God.——

1.
3. No

2.3.

What a won-der-ful God,——

what a won-der-ful God.—

(2nd time instrumental)

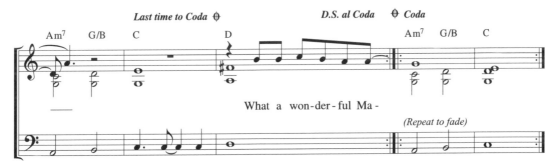

Last time to Coda ⊕

D.S. al Coda   ⊕ *Coda*

What a won-der-ful Ma -

(Repeat to fade)

148a In the beginning

Genesis 1: 1–4

In the beginning God created the heavens and the earth. Now the earth was formless and empty, darkness was over the surface of the deep, and the Spirit of God was hovering over the waters.

And God said, 'Let there be light,' and there was light. God saw that the light was good, and he separated the light from the darkness.

149   You're King and you reign

Geraldine Latty
& Carey Luce

3 part round

16 shuffle groove

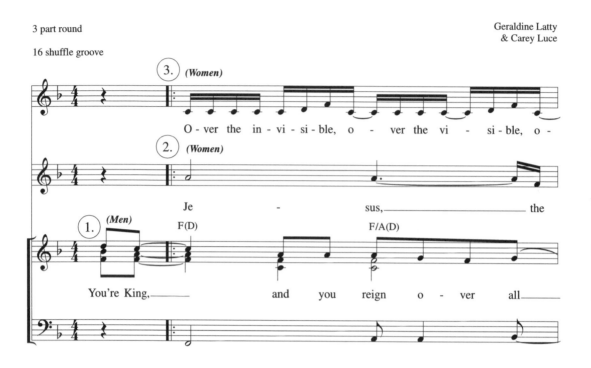

O - ver the in - vi - si - ble, o - ver the vi - si - ble, o-

Je - sus, _____ the

You're King, _____ and you reign o - ver all _____

ver all po - wers and king - doms. O-ver the in-vi-si-ble, o - ver the vi - si-ble, o-

glo-ry goes to you. Je - sus, _____ to

things. _____ You're King, _____ and you reign o - ver all.

150 You're the word of God the Father
(Across the lands)

Stuart Townend
& Keith Getty

♩ = 85

1. You're the word of God the Fa-ther,—— from be-fore the world be-
left the gaze of an-gels,—— came to seek and save the
shout you rose vic-to-rious,—— wrest-ing vic-t'ry from the

gan;—— e-v'ry star and e-v'ry pla-net—— has been fash-ioned by your
lost,—— and ex-changed the joy of hea-ven—— for the an-guish of a
grave,—— and a-scend-ed in-to hea-ven—— lead-ing cap-tives in your

hand. All cre-a-tion holds to-ge-ther—— by the po-wer of your
cross. With a pray'r you fed the hun-gry,—— with a word you stilled the
wake. Now you stand be-fore the Fa-ther—— in-ter-ce-ding for your

voice:—— let the skies de-clare your glo-ry,—— let the land and seas re-
sea.—— Yet how si-lent-ly you suf-fered—— that the guil-ty may go
own.—— From each tribe and tongue and na-tion—— you are lead-ing sin-ners

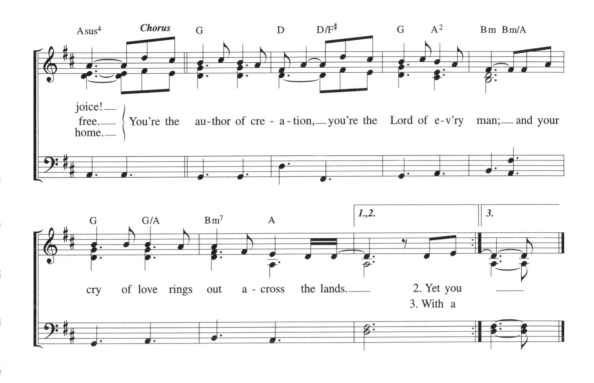

150a Sing to the Lord a new song

Psalm 98: 1–2

Sing to the Lord a new song,
    for he has done marvellous things;
his right hand and his holy arm
    have worked salvation for him.
The Lord has made his salvation known
    and revealed his righteousness to the nations.

Guitar Chords

Introduction

A good chord vocabulary is essential for a guitarist to feel confident when playing in worship, especially when the situation may involve reading a previously unseen piece of music or picking up a song quickly by ear. The chords on these pages are arranged in 'families' according to key. This is a beneficial way of remembering chords as most songs stick to these groupings. For each key, the first row shows the simplest form of each chord and the second line gives a more interesting substitution. The third line shows the chords most commonly used by guitarists derived by keeping some sort of pedal tone ringing in each chord and the fourth line shows inverted chords with an alternate bass note.

Also included are the Roman Numerals and Nashville Numbers associated with each chord. If you've not come across these before, they are simply an easy way of numbering each chord within a key. This is useful as it means you can take any chord progression in one key and instantly transpose it to another. For example, song No 40, 'He is the Lord', uses the chords G, C, D, Am which correspond to Roman Numerals I, IV, V, VI (or Nashville Numbers 1,4,5,6). A quick look at the chords for the key of E shows that those numbers give the chords E, A, B, F#m. So if you want to play this song in a small group but are concerned that the key of G is bit high, then it is a simple matter to transpose the song down to a more comfortable pitch. Furthermore you can try out any of the chords in each column that corresponds to the relevant Roman Numeral and see if there is chord type or inversion which still fits but adds a different flavour. Experimentation like this may open up creative chord progressions that serve as a catalyst to help you to worship in fresh ways or to write new songs.

Please see the CD-ROM section of Spring Harvest Distinctive Sounds album and the Academy of Music Ministry's website at www.nexustrust.co.uk for details of more material relating to developing these skills.

	Roman	I	II	III	IV	V	VI	VII
	Nashville	1	2	3	4	5	6	7
Key of C	3-note chord (triad)	C	Dm	Em	F	G	Am	Bdim
	4-note chord	C maj7	D m7	E m7	F maj7	G7	A m7	Bm7♭5
	Alternative substitute	C	D7sus4	E m7	F sus2	G5	A m7	Dsus4/B
	Alternative bass note	C/E	Dm/F	Em/G	F/A	F/G	Am/E	

For all chords in the key of C# or D♭, use the chords from the key of C with capo 1

Guitar Chords

Roman	I	II	III	IV	V	VI	VII
Nashville	**1**	**2**	**3**	**4**	**5**	**6**	**7**
3-note chord (triad)	D	Em	F#m	G	A	Bm	C#dim
4-note chord	Dmaj7	Em7	F#m7	Gmaj7	A7	Bm7	C#m7♭5
Alternative substitute	Dsus2	Em9	F#m7	G6sus2	A7sus4	Bm11	Aadd9/C#
Alternative bass note	D/F#	Em/B	F#m/A	G/B	G/A	Bm/F#	

Key of D

For all chords in the key of D# or E♭, use the chords from the key of D with capo 1

3-note chord (triad)	E	F#m	G#m	A	B	C#m	D#dim
4-note chord	Emaj7	F#m7	G#m7	Amaj7	B7	C#m7	D#m7♭5
Alternative substitute	E5	F#m11	G#madd♭6	Aadd9	Badd4	C#m7	D#alt
Alternative bass note	E/G#	F#m/C#	G#m/D#	A/C#	A/B	C#m/G#	

Key of E

For all chords in the key of F, use the chords from the key of E with capo 1

For all chords in the key of F# or G♭, use the chords from the key of E with capo 1

Guitar Chords

Roman	I	II	III	IV	V	VI	VII
Nashville	1	2	3	4	5	6	7

Key of G

	I	II	III	IV	V	VI	VII
3-note chord (triad)	G	Am	Bm	C	D	Em	F#dim
4-note chord	Gmaj7	Am7	Bm7	Cmaj7	D7	Em7	F#m7♭5
Alternative substitute	G	A7sus4	Dsus4/B	Cadd9	Dsus4	Em7	G/F#
Alternative bass note	G/D	Am/C	Bm/D	C/G	C/D	Em/G	

For all chords in the key of G# or A♭, use the chords from the key of G with capo 1

Key of A

	I	II	III	IV	V	VI	VII
3-note chord (Triad)	A	Bm	C#m	D	E	F#m	G#dim
4-note chord	Amaj7	Bm7	C#m7	Dmaj7	E7	F#m7	G#m7♭5
Alternative substitute	Asus2	Bsus4	C#m7	D6sus2	Eadd9	F#m11	Eadd9/G#
Alternative bass note	A/E	Bm/F#	C#m/E	D/A	D/E	F#m/A	

For all chords in the key of A# or B♭, use the chords from the key of A with capo 1

For all chords in the key of B, use the chords from the key of A with capo 2

Richard Stephenson & Andy Flannagan

Thematic Index
Numbers refer to songs, not pages

Praise and Thanksgiving (cont'd)

Prayer and Intercession

Proclamation

Proclamation cont'd

Renewal and Refreshment

Response

Scripture Index

Luke (cont'd)

John

John (cont'd)

Acts

Romans

1 Corinthians

Index of Liturgy and Prayers

Index of Bible Verses

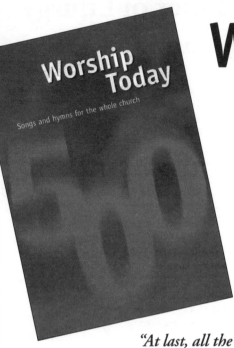

Worship Today

Worship Today is a unique resource that brings together the most popular songs and hymns being sung in the UK church today.

"At last, all the songs we're singing in one book ... "

Worship Today gives you:

- The top 500 songs and hymns – compiled using CCLI data
- A versatile resource – encompassing traditional hymns, old favourites and contemporary songs
- New layout – larger pages, fewer page turns
- Practical indexing – Thematic, Scripture, Alphabetical and keys
- Quality binding that lies flat on a music stand
- Liturgy, prayers and Scripture – to enrich your congregational worship
- Complete church resource – hardback words edition also available
- Permission to photocopy – CCLI's MRL licence holders can photocopy within the terms of their licence

Details – including a complete song listing – are available at www.worshiptoday.co.uk or phone Spring Harvest on 01825 769000.

Worship Today is published
by Spring Harvest

SPRING HARVEST
Equipping the Church for action

Equipping Christians to live actively, biblically and wholeheartedly for Christ — that's the goal of all that Spring Harvest does.

The Main Event

The largest Christian event of its kind in Europe — an Easter-time gathering of over 60,000 people for learning, worship and fun. The programme includes varied and inspiring choices for everyone, no matter how old or young, and no matter where you are in your Christian life.

Resources

- *Books* to help you understand issues that matter — prayer, family issues, Bible themes, workplace and more
- *Music albums* introducing new songs and showcasing live worship from the Main Event each year
- *Childrens resources* including popular music albums and songbooks
- *Songbooks* to introduce the best new worship material each year
- *Audio tapes* of teaching from Spring Harvest — a selection of thousands is available to choose from
- *Youth pastoral resources, songwords projection software, video services and more...*

Conferences

- *Youthwork the conference* — for volunteer youth workers, run in partnership with Youthwork magazine, YFC, Oasis Youth Action and the Salvation Army

- *At Work Together* to equip workers to effectively live and witness for Christ in today's challenging workplace.

SPRING HARVEST Holidays

Le Pas Opton is a beautiful four star holiday site on the French Vendée coast, exclusively owned and operated by Spring Harvest. Mobile homes, tents or your own tent/tourer — take your choice at this delightful resort where you'll find top quality facilities and excellent service.

Our aim at *Le Pas Opton* is to give you the opportunity for relaxation and refreshment of body, mind and spirit. Call Spring Harvest Holidays on 0870 060 3322 for a free brochure.

INVESTOR IN PEOPLE

For more information contact our Customer Service team on 01825 769000 or visit our website at www.springharvest.org

Spring Harvest. A Registered Charity.